Best of *Kweli*

Aster(ix) Journal

presents

Best of *Kweli*

Spring 2017

***

Edited by
Angie Cruz and Laura Pegram

BLUE SKETCH PRESS | PITTSBURGH

All works were previously published in *Kweli Journal* (www.kwelijournal.org)

and appear via permission of both *Kweli* and individual authors.

Published via Blue Sketch Press, Pittsburgh.
www.bluesketchpress.com

Best of *Kweli:* An Aster(ix) Anthology / Aster(ix) Journal
Edited by Angie Cruz and Laura Pegram— 1st ed.
ISBN (print) 978-1-942547-05-1 (trade paperback)
1-942547-05-6 (ISBN-10)

Cover Design by Little Owl Creative (littleowlcreative.com). Cover Collage by Aracelis Girmay (aracelisgirmay.net/). Sky image by Fabio Marini (flickr.com/photos/fabiomarini). Copy-Edited by Joseph N. Welch, III.

First Edition: March 2017

Printed in the United States of America
9 8 7 6 5 4 3 2 1

This compilation contains works that originally appeared in *Kweli*, an online quarterly that celebrates cultural kinships and the role of the literary imagination in writing.

Works have only been edited for grammar/ style and appear as they originally did on www.kwelijournal.org.

This compilation could not have been possible without the following Pitt MFA students who participated in various capacities as editors, proofreaders, organizers and/or visionaries: Rachel Ann Brickner, Ariana Brown, Stephanie Cawley, Hannah Eko, Eowyn Randall, Malcolm Everton Friend, Joshua Graber, John Kennedy, Kent Kosak, Clarissa León, Abigail B. Lind, Yan Pu, Lucia LoTempio, Gabrielle Marovavy Rajerison, Rachel Sterling, Suzannah Spaar, Angela M. Velez, Anna Weber.

Aster(ix) Journal

www.asterixjournal.com

Aster(ix) is usually published 2-3 times a year in print with additional content online.

Funded in part by the Dietrich School of Arts and Sciences and the Department of English at University of Pittsburgh.

Contents

Editor's Note

Angie Cruz with Laura Pegram

And who will join this standing up
and the ones who stood without sweet company
will sing and sing
back into the mountains and
if necessary
even under the sea

we are the ones we have been waiting for

—by June Jordan from Passion (1980)

I met Laura Pegram back in 2009 when she solicited my work for *Kweli*. I was one of the first writers she published in her journal. Soon after I made a date with her in NYC and since I have been inspired by Laura's resilience and optimism. She has faced incredible challenges but continues to nurture her writers and her journal, and is always full of ambition for what the journal can and will do. In the spirit of content spilling from one journal to another I have spent the past four months working with Pitt MFA students to cull through seven years of works published in *Kweli*. Together we selected twenty pieces. No easy feat. For the final conversation and selection, Laura Pegram joined us at University at Pittsburgh. The following is the conversation we had during her visit.

Angie Cruz: Let's start with you telling us how *Kweli* came about.

Laura Pegram: *Kweli* wasn't a definitive plan until I ended up in the hospital and then in a wheelchair, and my life, as I knew it, completely changed. By that point, I had been living with mixed connective tissue disease (MCTD) for over 20 years. Before I lost control of my legs, I had been actively involved in the arts community. I missed my contact with my students at Frederick Douglass Creative Arts Center (FDCAC), where I had been teaching workshops in the evening. They became my second family. But once I was released from the hospital, the only time I left the apartment was when two brothers from the Windsor Ambulette Service picked me up and carried me, in my wheelchair, down and up five flights of steps to and from New York Presbyterian to see my doctors. The ambulette service charged $200 a trip and it wasn't covered by insurance, so my home became a prison of sorts. I was newborn weak that first year. My days were structured around all things medical, but I could still dream, and I dreamed up *Kweli*. This literary baby became a distraction from the head pain, the fear, the doctor visits, all the long and protracted calls from the insurance companies. It took two and a half years to go from *Kweli* dream to *Kweli* reality. The journal became a way of continuing the work I had started as a writer, as an activist, from the convenience of my home.

It took time for me to learn how to walk again and it took time for *Kweli* to take its first steps. I invited some of my former students and colleagues from FDCAC to join as *Kweli* editors and board members. Trinee, Gena and Nicole would come to my small walk-up apartment and plan and brainstorm a vision. FDCAC was one of my greatest gifts.

Sadly, it is no longer in existence, but that was my home when I was a shy student who was learning and growing and developing my craft.

AC: Can you talk about June Jordan, who was your teacher?

LP: Ah, yes! June was not only my teacher, she was also my second mother, my mentor. She was an amazing poet, activist, and essayist. In college, June awakened me not only to what was going on politically in the world, but to my power as a citizen of the world. She was the introduction to my activism. She was also the person who told me that the sky was my ceiling despite my limitations. Autoimmunity is on the rise in the black community and it is difficult to diagnose. As an undergraduate, I was in and out of the hospital pretty frequently. And June was always there with books! Poetry books, fiction, non-fiction, plays. Flowers and laughter filled the room. No matter where I was medically, somehow June always had a way of making me laugh, seeing things through a more hopeful lens no matter how bleak they may have seemed at the time. She showed my early writings to her circle of writer friends, introduced me to artists who would become mentors on the page. They all helped me to build my confidence, to raise my voice beyond that whisper. So I'm eternally grateful to her for everything she taught me and brought to me.

AC: You are a writer, but you are focused mostly now on editing?

LP: My writing has taken a second seat to *Kweli*, but I am slowly carving out more time for my stories and poems. Working as an editor came about because I saw a need. I had a lot of friends telling me they were more accustomed to rejection letters than not, and a lot of them were giving up. Kind of moving away from their love of the art and what it could do, so I thought I could change that up a little bit.

AC: Unlike many journals where writers receive form letter rejections, you actually read all the submissions with care and give them feedback. Could you talk about that process a little bit? About how you work with writers?

LP: Yes. Out of all the things I do with *Kweli*, the one-on-one relationship with the writer is what I enjoy most. I love spending that time with them and their work, getting to know their process, what takes time and what is effortless. Talking with them about how to strengthen their work is one of my greatest joys. But it is also time consuming. One piece can go through twelve to twenty drafts and then there are the lessons on craft (compression, contradictions of character, etc.). I push them in the way June pushed me. If I submitted something to her for review, she didn't let me get away with anything. She would return my manuscripts with red marks on each page. But when it was ready, she would say, 'now, that's a story.'

AC: So much work!

LP: And the workload grows exponentially each day. I teach as well, at Poet's House for writers based in the NYC area, and then online. Some of my international students are based near Ramallah, Istanbul, Iran, Canada, so *Kweli* has a global reach. That started from the very first call for submissions that we put out. We sent word to VONA and Cave Canem–established entities of color–and we got submissions from across the globe. So that was surprising because I always thought *Kweli* would be this small, local community, but it blew up faster than I thought it would or could.

AC: In 2014, you invited a number of writers to be guest editors. How did you like that process? I mean, you had to give up control a little bit.

LP: I did, but I got a little bit more sleep! At that time we were a quarterly, and it was a lot of work to do developmental and line edits. You have to sacrifice so much to get it all done by deadline. The to-do lists get larger at the end of each day instead of smaller. That's just the way of the nonprofit world. They demand a lot, they want to know you're accountable. So yeah, the guest editors helped me out tremendously. They gave me some breathing room.

AC: I'm curious about your decision to make *Kweli* a nonprofit instead of a grassroots effort. Have you had to make changes now that you are accountable to a board?

LP: We have always had to be accountable to the board of directors. They were artist friends and colleagues who believed in the mission of *Kweli*. The makeup of the board has shifted a bit over time. But raising funds in the first three years was hard. You can't apply for grant funding in those first years. I was taking care of *Kweli* deficits out of my own pocket and my pockets weren't that deep after I became disabled, I was living off of a monthly disability check.

AC: For years you have been paying writers out of your own pocket, right?

LP: At first I was like, ok, I can handle this. We started out as a biannual. I'll make it work. But by the second year it was no longer sustainable. I knew we had to look at getting our nonprofit incorporation quick so that we could get charitable donations. That made it possible for us to get a couple dollars here and there, and to get grants funding too.

AC: *Kweli* has committed more and more resources to children's literature, publishing more YA authors and hosting an annual conference. Can you tell us a little bit about it?

LP: We held our first mini conference in 2010 in the courtyard of La Casa Azul Bookstore in East Harlem. It catered to writers of young people's literature as well as to writers of adult fiction and nonfiction. After a few years, we decided to scale back from this multi-genre effort. The Color of Children's Literature has been well received. We were inspired by Charles Johnson's article, "The Color of Children's Literature." Edwidge Danticat was our keynote speaker in April 2016, and we had a standing-room-only crowd. It was great, but we exceeded the limitations for the space we rented. We're hunting for a larger space next year and it looks like the New York Times Conference Center will be the home for our 2017 conference.

AC: So what were some of the takeaways? I know you had industry people there, what's the action plan to make change?

LP: One of the things we want to do is not only help emerging writers develop their craft, but then introduce them to the editors and the agents that can help them build a career. So at each conference we have agents, editors who are actively looking for writers of color. We allow them [conference attendees] to have one-on-one sessions for critiques with them.

AC: So what do you think could be a possible solution for the challenges in publishing right now?

LP: I think we definitely need more editors of color. There is such a dearth. The problem lies in compensation. Most people graduate from college with loans so they can't look at publishing, editorial salaries as a way to begin.

AC: Also it seems that editors are not willing to take risks. I know for instance a good number of latino/a writers with books who can't find a home for them. It's mind boggling when you can count on one hand how many books by latino/as are published each year. I can see why so many writers of color have given up.

LP: But the yeses come. I always tell folks who submit to *Kweli* that the yes will come. You just need one yes. One of *Kweli's* contributors just emailed me last week, and said that she has a publisher for her short story collection. After years of putting her work out there and getting no no no no nos, she got two yeses within one week. How's that?

AC: So it is persistence, but also it's about staying inspired. I found this quote by Junot [Diaz] that resonates with me. He said, "You know, vampires have no reflections in a mirror? There's this idea that monsters don't have reflections in a mirror. And what I've always thought isn't that monsters don't have reflections in a mirror. It's that if you want to make a human being into a monster, deny them, at the cultural level, any reflection of themselves. And growing up, I felt like a monster in some ways. I didn't see myself reflected at all. I was like, "Yo, is something wrong with me?" That the whole society seems to think that people like me don't exist?"

LP: I love that quote.

AC: We need to keep the pressure on about diversity in publishing but also make an effort to see each other. If we start internalizing not being seen, it can make us monstrous. Often when we do see our selves reflected back at us in the mainstream it's an exaggeration or a distorted version of who we are. For me, as an editor, the reason I was excited to revisit the works in *Kweli* and sift through it with the MFA students at Pitt is because there's so much content online. And I think this is one way we can create an opportunity to revisit content, so these important voices won't get lost in all the noise.

LP: Thank you for opening up our work to new audiences.

AC: Thank you Laura for introducing us to these amazing writers who are featured in this issue. And also I want to thank the Pitt MFA students who read the poems and prose with such care.

LP: Thank you so much, Angie. And many thanks to your students.

Ain't That Good News

Brit Bennett

Florence Holmes kept her knife in Psalm 94.

An eight-inch stiletto with a pearl white handle. Folks saw her walking around town, King James sticking out her purse, and they'd get to thinking she was holy now. That she'd found religion after what happened and all, like she was going to become a church lady, buy herself a big hat and sit in the front pew, white gloves up to her elbows. But the truth was that Bible was thick enough to hide the blade and she wouldn't go anywhere without either. She had a gun, too, of course. A shotgun under their bed, and a pistol her husband Barrett stashed in the glovebox, loaded and ready. But she didn't want to use the gun. For twelve years, she'd carried that blade in Psalm 94, hoping she'd be walking around town one day and out of nowhere, she'd see him. Andy Robinson, blond and lanky and looking into the open hood of a truck at the auto shop or playing basketball outside of Crawford High School, sweating and smiling, his arm curling toward the rim like a question mark. Florence wouldn't say nothing. She'd watch him a minute through the chain link fence—he wouldn't notice her, too busy panting and running up and down the court—and when he was standing by the metal bench, wiping his face with his shirt, she would sneak up behind him with Psalm 94 and shove that knife clean inside him.

Florence never had a question about what she'd do if she saw Andy

Robinson again. But that was before the sheriff caught him. Now the state of Louisiana was set to execute him, and Florence only felt sorry that she didn't get to Andy first, with her Bible and that beautiful blade. In her head, it was always the knife. She wanted to feel Andy's body collapse into that pearl white handle. She wanted to pull out the glinting silver and stick it in again, always into his side, never across his throat because that's the way you might kill a hog. Quick. Merciful. She wanted Andy Robinson to drain slow. She wanted to feel him twitch and fight to live. You couldn't get that with a gun.

***

Andy Robinson's death was set for September 3rd , 1993. Nobody knew the time nor the hour. *The Crawford Daily* said that on his final day, he would be moved to a cell near the execution chamber in Camp F, and the execution would take place any time between six PM and midnight. The only person who knew exactly when was the Warden; the rest of the inmates at Angola were never told when an execution was taking place so they wouldn't riot. Not that anyone would riot on behalf of Andy Robinson. Prisoners hate child killers.

When the *Daily* arrived at the Crawford Coffee Cup Diner that morning, everyone huddled around it, searching for details about the time of death. The cook thought it would be late. A waitress didn't see why, it wasn't like the governor was planning on calling to halt the execution at the last minute. Why not just get it over with, save everyone the trouble and time? The diner owner said they should just crumple the paper and toss it in the garbage before Florence and Barrett came in for their morning coffee, and everyone agreed that would be best. Most felt silly for wondering. Why did they care when Andy Robinson would take his last breath? He would be dead soon and that was all that mattered. There could be justice in Crawford, even for little Black girls, and the Holmeses were lucky to receive it. No one would have to think about the murder again. No need to hide the *Daily* when Florence and Barrett Holmes stepped into the diner, no need to smile extra wide when you led them to their booth by the window, no need to give them extra cream, extra sugar, extra butter for their toast, all the little extra things folks felt they deserved.

Florence and Barrett always sat in the back booth by the window. The Crawford Coffee Cup Diner was squat and long like a shoebox and Florence had to sit by the window or she felt like a trapped bug. Her husband liked to stare out the window although there was nothing to see except the faded gray parking lot, and beyond, the steel bridge stretching over the Calcasieu River that pointed toward New Orleans. But that morning, he turned from the window, cupping the steaming mug, and asked her to pick up ice cream after work.

"The ones with the little pecans in them?" he said. "Can you do that for me, honey?"

Florence knew what he was up to, but she didn't say anything. She leaned against the table and took a sip, her stomach squishing against the black rubber. She had put on weight in the past twelve years. She wasn't bothered by it—she had always been too skinny; the other kids used to laugh at her chicken legs and call her Olive Oyl—but she couldn't tell if Barrett had even noticed.

"We don't have any?" she said.

"Not that I seen."

"You look in the ice box?"

"Course. Where else would I look?"

He gave her a teasing smile, that same crooked smile she used to think was charming when they'd met thirty years ago.

"Why don't you just say it?" she asked.

"Say what?"

"That you don't want me to go."

"You already know I don't want you to go."

"Then why don't you just say it?"

"What I need to say it for if you already know it?" He shrugged. "It ain't civilized, Flo. Watching a man die."

The coffee was too hot, but she took a sip anyway, staring across the table at where Barrett's name was stitched across his heart. Under the table, she pressed her leg against her purse where the Bible bulged, the knife marking Psalm 94 instead of a gold ribbon. Barrett thought she carried the knife because she was afraid. She still remembered the way his eyes had flickered when he first saw it. For a second, Florence had thought he might let out a big laugh, the way he used to when she'd lock the car doors at the drive-in. *What you scared about*, he'd say, *don't you know I'm here to protect you?* But when she slipped the knife and Bible in her purse, his eyes touched the silver and he just nodded a little. She'd never told him she wasn't scared. She'd never been less scared in her life. She had just buried her only child, and she felt calm and steady like she was rocking on the porch swing. Moving, but still, still. Now ten years she'd been carrying that knife—even after Andy Robinson was found, even after he had been given death—and she planned to carry it until the moment she watched him drop dead. But it still wasn't enough. She wanted to dip her hands in Andy Robinson's blood like it was warm dishwater.

"Well, I guess I ain't civilized then," she said.

***

Wanting to kill someone felt like a type of love. Before they caught him, Florence worried about Andy as often as his own mama might: cotton soft thoughts, like was he fed? Was he bloodied? Was he well? Was he asleep at a bus stop? Did he remember to bring a jacket? Bet he forgot. Bet he never remembered to bring a jacket. He was on the run for three months, and all that time, she worried that he might catch cold or starve. The only thing worse than him getting away was him dying a natural death. She didn't want there to be anything natural about the way Andy Robinson left this earth. And she worried about him, praying that nothing or no one else would touch him until the sheriff got to him first. Now that he was locked away, she still thought about Andy every day, little thoughts that felt like touches in the dark. Just to reassure herself that she hadn't imagined him—that this long, lanky boy on the front page with those soft eyes had used his knobby hands to spread her daughter's thighs like a wishbone before he hogtied her with her carnation pink sweater and tossed her in the Calcasieu River.

Last night, Florence had cooked dinner and wondered what Andy would pick for his last meal. A porterhouse steak, maybe, or crawfish étouffée. She imagined herself surprising Andy. When he sat down for his final meal, she would ease on out the kitchen. Tie a napkin around his neck. Lay a silver tray in front of him and peel back the top to serve him the meal the sheriff's deputy had found in a Snoopy lunchbox along the riverbank: a crushed bag of animal crackers and half a sandwich with the crusts cut off.

***

After she left the Crawford Coffee Cup Diner, Florence stacked cans at the Market Basket. She didn't have an official job title. She'd started in high school as a bag girl, then a cashier who chatted with everyone who came through her lane. She smiled and asked *how was your day* and *mhm, did you see that picture of her in Jet* and *don't worry about it, I got an extra coupon right here*. But that was years ago. Now she just stacked cans. Her manager, Mr. Wilson, white but kind, set aside a gray stool for her, and each morning, she squatted on it and slowly built towers of green beans, peas, corn, chili, soup. Steady, simple work. One can on top of another, tiny circle inside a big circle. All morning long. She never talked to anyone. When folks came in to ask where something was, Florence just pointed. Aisle 4. Aisle 1. Back shelf.

That morning, Florence was stacking baked beans on the end of Aisle 3 when she heard a commotion near the front door. Mr. Wilson was standing in the doorway, hands on his hips, and when Florence poked her head out of the aisle, she saw Judy Robinson and her passel of children trying to push their way into the Market Basket.

Since the trial, Florence had only seen Judy from afar—crossing the street to the gas station, ducking into the laundromat—but she looked the same, ruddy with curly blonde hair. The only thing different about her was the litter of kids circled around her. During the trial, there had been one baby, a little girl Judy cradled while she cried on the witness stand and told the jury how Andy always helped take care of his little sister, how he held her real soft. How could someone that held a baby that soft do the things they said he'd done? It was someone else. He was just scared, that's all. That's why he ran. Not because he done it but because it was someone else and he was just scared. In the courtroom, Florence had wrung her hands, staring into the baby's blue eyes when she yawned or giggled or snuggled into her mama's neck. Now there were four children gathered around Judy, one pawing at her hip, the others chasing each other in front of the door, trying to dart past Mr. Wilson. Judy's eyes widened when she saw Florence.

"You stay back," Judy said, then to Mr. Wilson, "You keep her away from me."

"Get her out of here," Florence said.

She was gripping the can of baked beans as tight as she could. In her hand, it felt like a weapon. Like she could pin Judy Robinson on the checkered linoleum floor and smash the can into her face, for crying on the witness stand, for birthing Andy and the others after him, for daring to have all those kids in the first place. Florence's life had stopped in the last ten years, but Judy's had only started to bloom.

"I don't want trouble," Judy said. "I just wanna make my boy some cheesy grits."

"Well, go buy your cheesy grits some place else," Mr. Wilson said.

"I don't have time," she said. "They only let me see him til noon." One of her boys ran into her and she swayed, rubbing the buttons on the front of her dress. "Please," she said. "I don't need but one box."

"They ain't gonna let you bring in food from the outside," he said.

"All he asked me for was some cheesy grits," she said. "I don't need but one box."

"Lord almighty," Mr. Wilson said. "Go get your damn grits and get out of here, will you?"

He stepped aside, and the children ran laughing into the store, skidding on the checkered linoleum. Judy gave her one last look before disappearing up one of the aisles. Florence just squeezed the can of baked beans and watched her go. Mr. Wilson touched Florence's shoulder.

"Why don't you go work on your cans?" he said.

Steady, simple work. One right on top of the other. But when Florence gripped the stool under her, her hands were shaking. She bent, reaching for another can of beans, and when she straightened, there was the grubby little girl with fuzzy blonde braids standing next to her display.

"Bet I can reach all the way up there," the little girl said, pointing to the top of the stack.

She had to be around nine, with a chubby baby's face, but the way she stood there with her hands jammed in the pockets of her Mickey Mouse overalls made her seem older. She leaned back, eyeing the silver towers of cans, but Florence ignored her, reaching into her crate for another.

"What you gonna give me if I do it?" the little girl said. "A dollar?"

Her cheek was dusted with white powder, like she'd just stuck her whole face in a box of doughnuts or maybe just a bag of sugar itself, and Florence resisted the urge to lick her finger and swipe the sweetness away.

"A quarter?" the girl said. "Bet you a quarter I can reach it."

What kind of mama let her child go out looking like that anyway? Hair all over her head, food stains still on her cheeks.

"How about a penny? I'll do it for a penny."

She put the final can on top, then flexed her empty hands inside her lap. The little girl inched closer. She made Florence nervous, the way she stared with those big blue eyes.

"Go find your mama," Florence said.

"She's right there," the girl said.

She pointed at the checkout lane where Judy Robinson was standing with her box of grits.

"I tried to tell him," Judy told the cashier, digging into her fabric coin purse. "They're gonna get cold. Cheesy grits don't stay warm. But that's all he wanted. I tried to tell him. Why don't he listen to me?"

There was a crash. Florence jerked, and when she turned around, she saw her towers of cans scattered across the floor, the little girl next to them.

"I reached it," she said, "and you wasn't even watchin'."

***

The girl's name was Raylene.

Florence learned it quick enough, listening to the teacher holler at her every five minutes. Raylene, stop jumpin off those swings! Raylene, don't you dig up all that dirt! Raylene, what'd I tell you about cuttin' in line for the slide? You wait your turn just like everyone else. Around two, Florence sat on a bench outside Crawford Elementary School, her Bible in her lap, watching the children play through the chain link fence. Through the iron diamonds, the kids scrambled on top of the jungle gym, pushed each other on swings, and climbed across the monkey bars while the teacher walked back and forth, a whistle hanging from her neck. Only one teacher for all those kids. When Florence was sure, she tucked her Bible under her arm and crossed the street toward the corner of the playground where the teacher had sent Raylene to sit by herself.

"Raylene," she said.

The girl's name felt funny in her mouth. Raylene. A big name for a little girl with fuzzy blonde braids, but she turned around anyway, and when she saw Florence pressed against the fence, her fingers curled around the links, she smiled.

"You the can lady," Raylene said.

"Yep, that's me," Florence said. "Come on now, Raylene. You got to come with me."

Raylene squinted up at her. "How come?"

"Because your mama said." Florence shifted her Bible under her other arm. "She sent me for you. You got to come with me now. Your mama sent me to get you."

She thought Raylene might scream. Small part of her hoped it, even. But Raylene just glanced over her shoulder at the teacher—still strolling around the basketball court, swinging her whistle as she walked—and she hopped off the ground, dusting clumps of grass off the seat of her pants before she ran toward the fence opening. Too easy, Florence thought as Raylene came bounding toward her. Was it always this easy, just the whispering of a name through a fence? Maybe it was always that easy to do what you want, you just had to believe you had the power first. Maybe the hard part was the deciding to do it. Once that happened, everything else just glided right after it.

"Come on," Florence said. "We got to go."

She started walking faster now toward the crosswalk. She was starting to feel jittery. Of course someone would stop her. You couldn't just walk off with someone else's child. The teacher would spin around and see them, Florence in her green Market Basket polo shirt and Raylene in her grass-stained overalls, and she would know that Judy Robinson was white and young and thin and blooming, not this old Black woman with the graying hair, clutching a Bible to her rounded middle. Or one of the kids would point through the fence, hey where's Raylene going? Why's she get to leave early? Or even Raylene herself would finally remember something her mama had told her way back about not going off with strangers, no matter how friendly they look—why didn't children listen? why didn't they remember?—and she'd dig her heels on the sidewalk and refuse to go any farther. But there was no other sound except for the leaves scraping on the sidewalk and the chains from the swing rambling and children laughing in the afternoon sun.

Florence stepped off the curb and she felt Raylene take her hand as they crossed the street.

"Where we goin'?" Raylene asked. Her hand was soft, sticky.

"Just for a little walk," Florence said. "We're just gonna take a little walk first."

"Did my mama tell you she takes me for ice cream after school?" Raylene asked.

"Mhm. She sure did."

"Every day. She lets me get two scoops. Not just one."

"Mhm," Florence said. "We just gotta take a little walk first."

She was heading toward the river, and Raylene, still holding her hand, was scrambling to keep up. Florence had forgotten what it was like to walk alongside a child. Short legs, you had to slow down a bit. And then sometimes they dawdle. Amber always dawdled. Dillydallying, here and there, stopping to snatch a flower, bending to scoop a roly-poly onto a leaf, picking up lost buttons, bottle caps, paper clips. Nasty things you shouldn't touch, Florence always told her, swatting at her hand. You don't know where they been. And Amber, bright, used to say, I know where they been, right here on this sidewalk.

"What you readin?" Raylene said.

She was looking up at Florence with those blue eyes. Still the dash of white on her cheek that Florence wanted to wipe off with a dab of spit. But there was only a little bit further to go. The riverbank was up ahead, and under the leafy trees, no one would be able to see them from the road.

"What book is that?" Raylene said. "Can I see it?"

Florence clutched the Bible tighter under her arm. She could smell the river, the almost stale, almost sweet, murky brown water. She hadn't gone down here in years, not since she'd watched the sheriff's deputy pluck tiny floral panties out of the bushes. But the water smelled the same as it had when she and Barrett used to spend summer afternoons here, Barrett fishing, and Florence lying out under the trees, their baby sleeping against her breasts.

"Bet I can read it," Raylene said. "What you gonna give me if I can read it?"

"Shh," Florence said. She clenched her fist. She could still hear Barrett whistling, feel the downy babyhair on her fingertips.

"You gotta give me three scoops," Raylene said. "If I make it past the first page. Not just two."

"Quiet."

"When we gonna—"

"You shut up now!" Florence said. "You just shut up."

Raylene scowled, reaching for the Bible, and when Florence stepped back, trying to switch it to her other arm, the knife clattered out. That eight-inch stiletto blade with the pearl white handle hit the dirt between them. Raylene stared at it, then looked up at Florence, blue eyes big, and Florence knew she would scream, prepared herself to step forward and clamp a hand to Raylene's mouth, but the little girl didn't say anything. She just crouched to the ground, reaching for the knife.

"Stop!" Florence said, jutting her arm out. "Don't touch that!"

Raylene frowned and bent to pick it up again, but before her fingers raked against the handle, Florence grabbed her by her thin wrist and slapped her across the face. One hard little slap on her cheek, then another one. Raylene's blue eyes filled with water, and before she realized it, Florence dropped to her knees and cupped the girl's face in her hands and kissed her cheeks, once, twice, three times.

"You can't be touchin' things like that," she said. "You're gonna stick yourself. You don't wanna stick yourself, do you?"

Raylene shook her head. She sniffled, her shoulders shaking, and Florence smoothed down her shirtsleeves, fixed her face into a smile.

"You gotta listen to grown folks," she said. "You don't wanna end up bad like your brother."

"I don't know my brother," Raylene said. "He lives in a box."

Florence dipped her thumb in the river and wiped the stain off Raylene's cheek.

"My little girl does too," she said.

***

The Crawford Daily said that Andy Robinson prepared no final words. The Warden gave him two minutes to speak, but the man was silent as they strapped him onto the table. No words for the chaplain, who crossed his body, nor for his mama, who sat on the other side of the glass, holding a bowl of cheesy grits in her lap. Not for Florence Holmes, who was not standing in the back of the witness galley, who had missed the Warden's call about the time the execution was scheduled because she'd walked Raylene Robinson home before returning to the Market

Basket to find pecan ice cream for her husband.

According to the *Daily*, the Warden took off his glasses, which was the sign to begin. The machine started to push three different tubes of chemicals into Andy Robinson's body. But before his last breath came out like a snore, like the sound a balloon makes when you squish all the air out of it, before he coughed, sputtered, and gasped, before the eternal quiet, Andy Robinson spoke his last words. His eyes blinked open and he said, "I can taste it."

When she read it in the paper the next morning, Florence didn't know if he meant the drugs—did a chemical surging through your veins have a taste?—or his last meal coming back up. Or maybe he meant his regrets, maybe he'd swiped his tongue over his teeth and tasted blood or shame or his own life leaving him. Florence didn't know if death tasted like filet mignon or cold cheesy grits or a little girl's lunch, if death had a taste at all.

Volver, Volver

Ariana Brown

y volver, volver
to the mouth of the Yucatán
where we first glistened
with a stranger's tongue,
Spanish,
our old muscles bullied into
lovely wrecks &
our mothers wept
at the loss, for
they knew language
is the last sound
of war; & then
came the trumpets

volver
a tus brazos otra vez
my grandmother's
elementary, her inherited
Spanish trickling through
closed lips, as the teacher
instructs, 'English only';
& my grandmother

is an essay
on shame, a grito
trembling the walls
the color of sorrow

llegaré hasta donde estés
four years of Spanish classes
to remember the name
of grandmother's tears;
learning first
to pronounce each
syllable with the intent
of a conquistador - if
I am to grieve properly,
give me my language with
which to do it

yo se perder, yo se perder
black as a young moon, I
am spoken to in English,
the third tongue, final
conquest, never mistaken
for indigenous, never pain,
never daughter of woman
who hums mariachi songs
in crowded restaurants,
skimming lyrics in favor
of memory; & all I want
is permission to love
the gaps in my lineage
as one would the breaths

in a favorite song

quiero volver, volver
volver
& when our tongues spin
in ways we don't understand,
I open the ancient faucet, let
memory guide this
new music until it is
the shape of something
I can hold,
close, like a prayer,
& I forgive the chaos
violence has left me
& I worship my
flexible sound
& I kiss my lover
with the mouth
I own.

Grandpa's War: An Anthem

Cortney Lamar Charleston

To hear voices in the hollow of a spent shell casing, or salute a spine at half-mast, or put on the uniform that is my family name: whichever it is, I'm sitting at this kitchen table, talking to my father's father. His tongue tends to get stuck on the same stories like the trigger of a jammed carbine, coughing on things that should've passed through like the shape of a life through wall, but no. His stories bleed together: comrades fallen in a field far from home. I have their dog tags in pocket, but I play audience anyway. With every exchange, he explains that he's inching closer to the grave, and I suppose a soldier thinks in no other way; the last step is freshest in the dirt, and since I grew old enough to read the writings on the wall, our relationship has been his feet coming clean to me: clear water.

See, Grandpa was with the Signal Corps in France. Came back another black veteran with his signals crossed, says the word *nigger* as if he believes they actually existed. I'm confident he can use a gun. Used to wonder if he ever killed someone in a name that wasn't his own. Never asked him. Eventually found out he pointed the barrel in that direction, and felt my curiosity cool, as willingness is the only gunpowder any man ever needed. He tells me he felt threatened, so he returned a threat in kind. Black men then didn't have the luxury of moral absolutes. Bravado had to be his bread when broke was brother in barrack. The army was segregated just like everything else was, and he never forgets to mention it. And I know Grandpa will deny belief in specters, but I've spectated his fists forming as fully as thoughts of revenge inside empty rooms. Those knuckles can still feel the cheekbone of his commanding officer; I wonder if it feels like justice or simply feels just. After all, pride predates honor and I'm not sure on which side of the latter he was born. I know Mississippi molded him like red river clay, that he knows no fear in fighting, that he has only flinched twice in his lifetime. The first time was Margie, my grandmother. The second was fatherhood. I know he drove a truck for his livelihood, that he owned it himself, that his wife delivered ten children while he made deliveries, and I know he softens whenever we meet eyes, so maybe, after all this time, he's finally letting go of all the bones to pick, toothpick still dangling on his lip like a cuss.

Guácala

Geimy Colón

Segundo bows his head, the face that makes people run now hidden from full view. His hands are still, resting over his knees. He watches his mother Clara at the altar holding a tiny piece of Paco's dried belly button. She prays over it before pressing it between the pages of her bible. She plants a kiss on Paco's photo, then another kiss on Segundo's forehead, and ushers him out of the bedroom. This has been her everyday ritual for the past year, ever since his wicked game with Paco in the soil.

Segundo goes back to finish his sweet plantain at the dining table. He waits. When his father honks the car horn he jumps up in his chair. Clara rushes to the front door holding a business suit his father needs laundered. "Glenny, watch Segundo. And forget Menudo. Watch him." The suit floats with her like a ghost made of grey cloth.

"Ma, take me," Segundo says as she leaves. Clara does not hear him through the music floating out of Glenny's cassette player. She disappears into sunlight, her gardenia perfume trailing behind her. Glenny rolls her eyes, the reluctant summer babysitter. She sets a white pill down hard near Segundo's plate. He stuffs it deep into his pants pocket and then runs as fast as his short legs can carry him, away from the apartment. Away from Glenny's loose hands.

"Take the medicine for your heart defect," Glenny calls after him, but he is out of the apartment without minding her or her rules, without minding his face or his misshapen heart.

In no time Segundo finds a broken tricycle. He plays alone with the bike outside the apartment complex. Some of its parts are scattered around on the ground. He collects the parts into the hem of his shirt saying, "Mine, mine, and mine," before wheeling the tricycle toward Proeza's courtyard. The back wheels squeak as they turn when he reaches the yard.

Traffic buzzes behind him on Máximo Gómez Avenue as he works on the tricycle with his hands only. He wraps the front wheel around its small rim; realigns the back wheels; steps onto the crooked cross-bar and straightens it with his weight. He rotates the handlebar until it tightens and bangs on to the seat once, twice. The seat snaps it into place. At twelve years of age he has never ridden a bicycle and does not know the feeling.

"They left you," he says to it. "But I got you." "Mi Moto," he names it as he brushes dirt off the tiny pedals.

In fewer than five minutes, he is holding a near-new tricycle. It is less broken as he turns the handlebar—left, right—to see how the front wheel moves.

"Not garbage! No, no, no, no, no," he says to it. Segundo does not play like other boys his age. His toys are the things he builds.

Always in motion, his hands are expert at scavenging, and are forever gathering, fashioning structures out of something his feet trip over, especially if school is out, like now that it is August. This week alone: Arranging salvaged wood planks and cinder blocks into shelves for his big sister's one thousand books on Monday. Repurposing rubber tires into flower planters for his mother on Tuesday. Crafting a tie rack for his father out of twigs and twine on Wednesday. Erecting cardboard forts that held in strong winds on Thursday.

Today is Friday and Segundo is caressing the tricycle when two boys pass him in the courtyard. They stop a few feet away from him, standing near a palm tree. One of them puts his index fingers into the corners of his own mouth, tugs down hard, and sticks his tongue out at Segundo. He waggles his tongue around and makes air bubbles with his saliva. The other boy scampers about orangutan-style, exaggerating each movement, his hands sweeping low and in wide arcs over the green-green grass.

"There goes Bob the Builder!" one says to the other.

"That bike's falling apart when he sits his fat Weeble Wobble ass on it!"

Both cackle. They say nothing to Segundo. Neither one looks straight at him. When Segundo opens his mouth to say something, the other two run off, racing each other. He hangs his head; looks down into his own hands, alone again.

His hands are so adept at handling inanimate objects that he does not understand how they break the living things he yearns to touch. At five years of age an egg he stole from a hen to warm till hatching time, and which he crushed on the way home. At seven, earthworms he fondled until they shriveled in his pocket while in his seat at the Batey School for Exceptional Learners. At nine, a frog he dissected with a sharp rock, and which he tried to put back together with rubber cement. At eleven, just one year ago, Paco, his little brother, in that game.

"Mi Moto," says Segundo and circles the tricycle, inspecting it. A toy headlight rests on the ground beside him. He grabs it and presses it onto its base on the handlebar. Plastic snaps into plastic. It holds!

"Take you home." Segundo wheels it through the courtyard with one hand, stooping low enough to fall head-first. He is big for a twelve-year-old. He has a long-long torso and short legs with the girth of tree trunks. With every move, everything about him rolls in every direction; his face leads the way.

Palm trees stand like soldiers in formation along the perimeter of the courtyard. The wind kicks up, ruffling long palm fronds. He looks up at a small flock of wild parrots that caws past in flight.

A little girl walks into the yard and jumps when Segundo flashes his smile. She stops cold, frowns, looks about. He takes a few steps forward, still holding the tricycle, his free hand with short fat fingers splayed. The girl walks backward fast. She runs away, he follows, pointing back at the tricycle.

"Mamá, Mamá!" she screams, running toward a woman who is standing near the front of the complex, close to the avenue. The woman calls her over with one hand.

The complex is a city within a city. There are pastel colors as pale and bright as sunshine on every building. Behind the woman: two semicircles of apartment buildings stand opposite each other. These buildings are ringed by repeated rows of other four-story buildings with stacks of identical, coral-pink terraces. Their patterns make Segundo trip. Segundo stops short and bends at the waist. He places a hand across his heart and rubs the spot. His heart is speeding up at will. He forgets the pill, gulps air. The complex stretches out around him in all directions.

The precise layout of the complex often leaves him near vertigo, and causes him to lose his way on the paths of the adjacent developments. He has been losing his way ever since he learned to walk, at age two and a half, and once he started wandering past the repeating facades, unaccompanied. He glances up at the girl.

"Mamá! Make him disappear," she wails as her eyes bulge. She reaches her mother, twisting around her to shield herself with the woman's body. She cries louder.

From a few yards away, Segundo watches the woman reach behind her back to hold her daughter with both hands. She shoots a look at him; her mouth tight, her eyes hard like the walls behind her.

"Come … I found it! Broken. Mi moto. I fix it," Segundo says. He bares his teeth in a smile like a grimace. Neither one addresses him.

"Don't even look at him," the woman says. The two turn their backs to him and speed-walk away, bodies clasped. They leave him standing there, all smiles and arms outstretched.

Segundo's face, over-eager, smiling hard, and in constant pursuit, says PLAY WITH ME NOW to anyone who crosses his path.The kids in his neighborhood dart in every direction when his face meshes into a smile that spreads wide and sets into a floppy mask. He has wide-spaced teeth encircling a tongue that does not fit in his mouth. His cheeks droop in folds, and spit collects where his overgrown bottom lip hangs open, so loose that you can see down to the purple gum line, as he drools, until he tucks in his lip and swallows.

There is no one else to play with in Proeza's courtyard. Segundo stashes the toddler-bike behind some shrubs. He gives the seat one last loving pat before walking away.

"Mine. My friend, Moto," he says to it. He feeds his hunger for people with the broken things he repairs; Segundo is ravenous for friends.

Uno and Boca Chula were his only friends in the District. They chose him one day when they observed what he could do with his hands and no tools: he built them a small sturdy hut, using only twigs and soft plant stems to tie the sticks together into walls and a roof, draping a sheet over it to complete it. He could do things with his hands that they could not, and he made them toys they could not buy. So they forgave his face.

They would wait for him every day at dismissal, hiding behind the Batey School's perimeter wall, until Segundo would appear through the gates, one able body in a procession of helmets, wheelchairs, and boxy walkers, all reflecting sunlight. Segundo was one of the few steady on their feet, ambulating among children with bionic limbs who handled their crutches like extensions of themselves, fused aluminum and steel wings, folded for walking.

They moved away mere days after their game with Paco, last year. Their families stayed only as long as it took to pack clothes, photo albums, and important documents. A neighbor swooped in to rescue whatever was left in corners and behind doors, purses and belts and crucifixes hanging from nails.

Segundo's shadow cuts into the sunlight gleaming over the grass. He watches the wind become visible in bits of trash that rise and twirl up into the air before him, in a ten-foot funnel. It lifts debris into itself, moving forward, then splitting apart, and dropping litter here, there. A plastic bag catches air and fills up like a sail; it floats away.

Crossing the yard in a straight line, Segundo takes a corner exit and disappears into the shade of the walled corridor that leads to the street. He exits at the other end and clangs the gate shut. Stooping down, he picks up an empty bottle lying in the gutter. Plastic crackles in his hand as he crumples the bottle like it is tissue paper. He heads to the park across from Máximo Gómez Avenue.

Every day, Segundo is fixated by the things others discard; he studies how they travel and disappear. He tracks the places where these things accumulate and are gobbled up, whole. Everywhere in the National District, he sees garbage he obsesses over, to reuse and make new.

This garbage makes of the streets his marked trails: at the nearest intersection, faded canvas sneakers swaying from electrical wires, laces tangled; one tiny Converse pair the size of Paco's feet. One block down, by his mother's church, clumps of artificial hair and glossy cassette ribbon hanging from forked tree limbs dotted with shredded newspaper woven into nests. On the next street, a brown baby-doll stuck in the branches of a dried out shrub. And a framed portrait of his city sprawling to the Ozama River's edge propped against a light post on the way to school.

Trash carried by rainwater into storm drains, mounded high on barges and falling over their sides; flowing downstream; lining the riverbanks—leading his way to and from the avenue. These things teach him the way through his expanding neighborhood. They indicate where he should turn right, left, and cross; where he should walk straight, stop, and keep going. They are his markers home, and his path to everywhere else. They make him troll the city for treasures every day with or without his parents' permission, with or without Glenny's violent eyes tracking him. And when some key part of this trash disappears, if he goes too far, he must all of a sudden relearn the way.

Segundo walks through the litter of his neighborhood sniffing for the nearby river. He wipes drool from his chin with his forearm. Today the city smells of motor oil and water vapor. Other thick odors hit him full-on, as if he is breathing through each one of his enlarged pores—cuchifritos, roasted peanuts, corn on the cob, hot asphalt, tar.

A loud rumbling moves down the avenue. The smell of rotten oranges fills the street. One step, two steps, three, and then Segundo freezes in place to stare. A white monster-vehicle slows to a crawl. It rumbles and vibrates, then stops, hissing. Two men dump things in. Lift, heave, dump, and repeat. Lift, heave, dump, and repeat, together, like this, moving on down the block, the two separate to gather things left a bit far from the curb.

Segundo's mouth hangs slack as he bugs at how refuse disappears into the back of the slow-moving garbage truck. And he marvels at the green drool of its enormous mechanized tongue when it clamps down on bags that burst open and leak before vanishing. He sees the truck swallow a sofa, a loveseat, and an armchair—an entire furniture set, gone!—in one hydraulic gulp. He wonders where those things go, and if they ever return.

"Everything in your belly," he tells the garbage truck as it creeps to the intersection. "Not my bike!" he says and sticks his tongue out at it.

The neighborhood is lit up in the highest light of day, under a mean August sun. The avenue's hum fills his ears. People everywhere sweat, not moving beyond the avenue. Some sell, some buy. A church bell sounds off. A woman in a house dress flies up St. Barbara's front steps for midday mass. Her head is a rainbow of hair rollers.

Segundo walks one block. His heavy footsteps are noiseless in the deep bass of commerce at the vendor stands spanning the avenue. Boys half his age sell coconut candy in traffic. Furry black flies circle pyramids of goods, buzzing. People wait in lines with fingers curled around folded dollar bills. A man jangles coins in a loose fist.

He stops at the intersection and pans his head from left to right, roving the scene for building supplies. Across the avenue: There is the sugar-cane-juice stand with big bundles of six-foot cane stalks, standing upright. The frituras, the Johnny cake, the coconut-water spots. Three-foot-tall vats of boiled corn cobs set on metal stands that sport enormous tricycle wheels.

A man with a wok of roasted peanuts placed over a rolled up towel on his head calls out, "Maníce, maníce, maníííceee!"

"El manícero," Segundo whispers and reaches into his pocket for money. Some coins clink against his heart pill. He forgets the peanuts and pops the white pill into his mouth, gulps it down dry. Then he hears a ruckus.

There—beyond the vendors and past the bus turnaround—a group runs in the park. The group changes shape and twists into itself, with big kids and little kids running together in the same direction, then fast in another, cornering some invisible thing, contracting, taking off suddenly, expanding, and turning in wide arcs as a single mass.

Segundo smiles that foot-long smile and hurries to join the revolving mob. His bottom lip hangs loose, but he pushes it back up with two fingers.

Half a dozen motorcycles zip past, weaving through traffic like fire ants. Cars. Honking. Sputtering. Hot air. An opening. Segundo hurls himself at oncoming traffic and crosses.

"Run, kid!"someone in the group shouts.

Segundo enters the park. The bulge around his middle makes him wobble-trot. He catches up. The group rolls toward him with its many arms and legs. He knows almost every face he sees, but they are not his friends. Some, those from his complex, know about his little brother, Paco, and some do not.

"Come ON."

"Why you so SLOW?"

"It's leaving!!! Block it!"

"What?"

"NOW, now. Get it!"

"But what?"

"Go, Segundo, go. It's running toward you!!!"

"Where, where?" Segundo asks. He sees only legs and feet flashing across trampled grass, and through these, more legs.

"Catch it, catch it!"

"What? What is it?!"

The group continues to move to the left, to the right, then away, and back again.

"You see it?"

Segundo looks everywhere, searches the area at the tips of pointed fingers, but cannot see the target.

"He can't keep up with it."

"What? Where?"

"There! Right there! Grab it!"

The group moves closer to Segundo and splits apart a little.

And then, through a gap in the bodies, he sees what the group is chasing: a chick!

"What a mongólico Segundo is!" They mimic his eyes, slits on either side of a flat-bridged nose.

"Go, go, GO!!!"

The chick runs past him. Segundo runs toward it. Now he sees it in slow motion.

Its pink skin glistens through partings in damp feathers. Its eyes bulge, layered by rings of wrinkled skin. A sliver of tongue pokes out of its beak. This is not a newly hatched, fluffy chick, all yellow cuteness, but one of those with a long neck and long legs, in that awkward stage between chick and adult. It has a spiky line of red flesh growing out of its head.

Goose bumps form all over his skin.

"Guácala. UGLY!" Segundo shouts at its head, which is squashed in on both sides.

The frantic chick takes off again. Segundo follows.

"Don't let it get away!" he hears, and runs faster, to catch up. He and the group chase the chick farther into the park, running up a slight hill. Segundo runs and bends and runs and bends. With arms out, he ducks, reaches, misses every time, almost at its tail. Drool stretches into a see-through string over his chin, falling as he moves. The chick runs with its head held high, going beyond the grass and onto a path lined with benches. Then it falls down the stairs to the paved monument square below.

The group breaks over the stairs like water splitting around the sharp edges of rocks. They collect around the monument and roll onto grass. Segundo shoves his way through the group. He hops around the chick from side to side, with arms outstretched and feet spread far apart sumo wrestler style. The group forms a circle around boy and chick.

"Cockfight!" someone yells, and everybody laughs.

Locked into the frenzy, Segundo throws himself on the ground and lands on his belly with a great heave. His hands wrap around the chick. Its heart thunders against his palms. He rises to his knees and stands, holding it. The chick's legs are crossed under its body, the digits of its scaly feet curled back, black dirt stuck in its claws.

The onlookers' voices blend with his own super loud heartbeat; the two sounds fill Segundo's ears. He cannot think. He swallows hard, breathes through his mouth. His eyes are as wide-open as the chick's. He holds it up in the air like a trophy, cupped in both hands. Its beak parts in rapid pants; it turns its head from one side to the other to look out of each eye.

"HE. CAUGHT. IT!"

"He's slow, but—."

"Look at his crazy people eyes! He's all EXTRA."

"Now he thinks we want to play with him!"

"YUCK!"

Segundo walks along the inside of the circle, his chest rising and falling fast. He forms an "o" with his mouth and puffs out deliberate shallow breaths to slow his own heart—a trick he learned at the Batey.

Segundo thrusts the chick at the group, some kids pull away from him. A boy shoves him back into the circle, but wipes both hands on his shirt.

Segundo stumbles, laughing. Now he is holding the chick by the head. Its body dangles at his side. A girl who lives in his building points at him with scared eyes. A few kids clap, some cheer, others do not move or make a single sound. Standing in the middle of the circle, Segundo takes a slow 360-degree spin to look into every face until his own face breaks into a wide, saggy smile. They looking at me, all looking at me, is his only thought, and the thought amps up his heart.

"What you gonna do with that nasty chick?" a boy asks.

In a nanosecond, Segundo starts swinging his right arm in big, steady circles, round and round, as if rearing up for the fastest pitch in the ballpark. They laugh as he swings the chick around nonstop. He looks at his own arm—up-down, up-down, up-down. And just when it looks like the chick will fly out of his hand, Segundo jets away. He wobbles up the stairs, cuts between two benches and down the hill. Winding back across the lawn, he jogs out of the park and to the avenue.

The group sweeps across the six-lane avenue, breaking up into traffic, running through it as cars brake, now following the boy with the chick that hangs limply from his hand.

The chick's limp body is like Paco's body a year ago, arms and legs dangling from his father's arms. Unsupervised, Segundo and his little brother, Paco, played a game with Uno and Boca Chula. The game: "Play Dead." Each one of the four was to take a turn being buried alive. "Like at the beach," Uno said. Uno was the oldest of the three and he called out the orders.

"Cuz not one of us is punkin' out," Uno said. "We're all doin' it. Paco is the littlest one, so he's first. My grandfather has shovels. Let's get them so we can finish faster!" "Let's go," said the other three. The four walked into the sun with Segundo hurrying to catch up.

They proceeded with great relish, flinging dirt, laboring to keep soil from sliding back into the hole. They took no breaks. Then, they borrowed two buckets and a small wagon from Segundo's garage. And they made a sizeable hole in no time, but still, they dug some more.

As Paco crawled in, Segundo held one of his small hands and did not let go until the smaller boy said, "Ok," and pulled out his hand with a little yank. Paco lay in the hole, sucking on the hard candy they bribed him with to go first. Segundo produced the candy out of his fingers like a magician. He removed the wrapper with a flourish, and handed it to Paco, their soiled fingers touching for a second as the candy passed from one brother to the other. And he was gentle when, at Uno's command, he covered Paco's face with a sheet of lined paper to keep soil from getting into his eyes, nose, and mouth. "No bugs," Paco said, and Segundo understood.

They filled the hole fast and packed it down as hard as they could, walking around and leaving their footprints in the soil. Then they sat on the ground, directly above Paco, sweaty and with dirt stuck under their nails, wondering what it is like to be dead. The intense heat muted the sounds of the neighborhood. No breezes blew. Two minutes passed and Segundo pressed his ear against the ground, listening for his little brother.

Paco died of asphyxiation three minutes later.

They buried Paco in the heart of the National District in a cemetery without paths.

The day after the burial, Segundo pressed his ear against his parents' bedroom door, listening for his mother. Instead, he heard his father's voice coming through the door.

"Clara, I'm beginning to love Segundo less."

Tomas had questioned Segundo about Paco's death. "He said it with a blank stare, Clara. 'I don't know.' No feeling, no remorse. Not a single tear . . . like he has no heart."

"You know he never thinks too far ahead, or back, that he cannot. That he … he lacks that capacity. Segundo couldn't have intended Paco's death."

"That's called involuntary manslaughter!"

"NO! With Segundo there is no consequence. It's something he can't measure."

"They buried him ALIVE, Clara. And he says he doesn't know? Like he couldn't save him?"

Segundo had pointed straight down at the ground when his father arrived from work and asked, "Where is Paco?" When he pounced on the small mound, it was too late to pluck out his youngest son. Still, he got on his hands and knees, and crawled on all fours in his navy blue business suit, his tie dragging on the ground as he scratched at the soil with his bare hands, feeling around for the boy, refusing to use the shovel that was lying nearby.

When they dug him out of the ground Paco's hands were still, and so was his chest, his flawless Betty Boop lips slack. His face was clean where the sheet of paper had been, but the rest of him was coated with soil. Soil fell from his limp body when they carried him inside with Segundo following the trail.

Tomas cried so hard people restrained him.

Everyone within a half-mile radius of his block heard the man's wild, wild howling.

Segundo stared and stared at the two spots where his father's perfect pant creases disappeared into the soil stuck to his knees.

And at the funeral, they saw him hop—up-down, up-down—ashen with grief, with eyes clenched shut, his face a deep grimace.

"Crying more than a woman," said some of the elder ladies, and men, shaking their heads in disbelief for so long that they forgot they were still saying, "no, no, no, no, no."

"His beautiful boy, four-and-a-half years old."

"And now left with the other one … with that mouth."

Segundo heard it all chewing with his mouth open standing by the platter with a pyramid of sandwiches cut into tiny white triangles.

A year later, and his father still does not look him in the face.

"Tomas, don't make me defend him as my heart breaks in two for Paco."

"Paco was the only person, besides you, who could look at Segundo with love in his eyes!"

"Eyes you never had for him, not even when they took him from my chest and he clung to my cheeks with both hands, crying out each time they tried to pull him away to stick him in that incubator. I saw how you looked at him!"

"I wasn't ready!"

"And then, when I could only see him through glass and his little heart was so wild that it was beating through flesh and bone. You were nowhere to be found."

"Must be I'm as incapable of loving him as he's incapable of reasoning."

At that, his mother let out a sob so loud and long and ragged it made Segundo jump away from the door as if it had scalded him.

At the third sob, Segundo ran to his room and sat before the small altar, with Paco's memory haunting the saints and the statue of Baby Jesus surrounded by his things—his baptismal hat and handkerchief, his pictures arranged like a martyr around the statue, and the smooth stones they brought back from the river arranged into a heart. The saints' eyes followed his every move when he sat at their feet.

"Uno's gone … Boca Chula's gone … Paco's gone," Segundo whispered to his mother's saints, uttering his own one-word novena.

They found him kneeling before Paco's photo with the candle still unlit, his head in a deep bow. When Clara bent to look into his face, there were wide tear tracks on his cheeks, his perpetual smile erased. She wiped his chin first with one hand and then with the other. A drool stain spread across his chest, soaking into his t-shirt. His sister Glenny tucked a small hand towel into his shirt collar. She spread the towel across his chest with gentle hands.

The chick is a white blur moving across the road. Cars swerve to avoid the last of the group crossing the avenue.

Segundo enters the complex with the group at his heels. Sneakers stomp down the entrance ramp. People turn to look at them as they reach the front courtyard, where they stop and regroup, before moving deeper into the complex.

Segundo leads, twirling the chick by the neck high above his head. When he brings down his meaty hand to look at it, its closed eyes startle him. The eyelids are grey and beneath them the eyeballs are sunken. His skin breaks out in goosebumps. He drops the chick. It does not move when it falls to the ground.

The group is silent. They stand still, watching the animal.

Segundo does not grasp death. He pokes it with the tip of his shoe. Nothing happens.

The kids turn from the chick to Segundo, who is mute. His lips part, saliva flows. The group makes the connection explicit for him.

"ASSASSIN!"

"Assassin!" echoes another.

Then every single voice, in unison: "Assassin! Assassin! Assassin!" They point fingers at Segundo. Chanting, the group closes in on him until his back is flat against the sidewall of a building.

"Assassin, assassin, assassin!"

They chant until he cries without a sound, looking down at the mangled chick. Its feathers sparkle in the sun, flattened where his fingers pressed too hard, earlier. He hiccups a huge sob. His bottom lip quivers when he looks at them one last time.

"Assassin!"

Segundo runs. Behind him, the group chants and laughs, still pointing.

"Assassin!"

The avenue fades.

"Assassin!"

He does not turn back.

"ASSASSIN!"

Nobody follows.

Paco would follow Segundo whenever he could. Two months before the accident, Segundo and Paco planned an escape to their favorite place. The Ozama River.

"Get down," Segundo says.

Paco gets down on the floor, on all fours.

Segundo assumes his position, standing next to him. He hesitates.

"Now," Paco says.

But—" Segundo tilts his head to one side and listens for his mother.

"Ready!" Paco sets off crawling fast, right out of their bedroom door. Segundo waddles down the hall, hurrying to step ahead of his little brother.

"Be invisible," is his only hard-whisper to Paco.

In this way, Segundo using his legs as a shield, and Paco crawling, they cut through the living room, passing potted aloes and macramé plant holders hanging from the ceiling. As allies, covering each other, they move from one piece of furniture to another, ducking, straining to become invisible, avoiding their mother, until they reach the front door and step out.

"Take me to the river, Segundo!"

Some of the streets that bisect Segundo's neighborhood run smack into the river and its smooth stones. Wide and narrow, gravel or cobbled, paved and unpaved, some end at the turbid water, and there, other streets begin. Whenever Paco goes with him, Segundo takes the straightest route to get there and back before sundown.

"This way … come!"

The brothers go on a mission, holding hands at intersections to cross streets. Neither one is phased when the houses change from concrete to slatted and wooden. Neither turns to look at the rows they pass, some houses without doors and dark, without electricity, arranged on a steep incline, with gravity pulling them into a near run when they finally cross the invisible line between the urbanized side of town and the part where no development projects have been ordered or financed by President Joaquín Balaguer.

The sloped trail of wild grass is interrupted everywhere by discarded plastics like confetti. The soil is so moist their feet sink as they near the river.

The Ozama River feeds into the sea, and so it smells of salt and seaweed.

Segundo traces its scent all the way to the edge, leaving behind the back paths of the complex. Paco is his shadow.

"I smell it," Paco tells Segundo, running ahead of him.

The brackish water forms a rich estuary where sea and river life incubate together. Each day at low tide the river's edge crackles with newly hatched life. "Every species in the ocean spawns here," Tomas swore to Segundo and Paco as he shook out a net on a day out catching crawfish. Clara and Glenny retrieved a pot of spaghetti and bread from the trunk. It was their last family outing, mere months before the deadly game.

Segundo's favorite spot of the river basin is a forest of exposed roots, tangled and tall. The spot is encircled by mangrove trees with roots knobby and gnarled like a giant's arthritic fingers, rising out of the water. The two stop before reaching that spot.

"Check under rocks!" Segundo calls to Paco.

"I am." Paco obeys stepping between rocks. "Look. The little holes!"

"ALL OVER," Segundo shouts, approaching.

"I WIN," says Paco.

"How?"

"I found them first," Paco says and grins.

Segundo admires the network of tiny crab-holes. He stomps around here and there. His footprints fill with groundwater with every step.

They appear and disappear in the wet sandy soil wherever his feet sink into the loose earth, disrupting numberless crabs, which break through the surface, claws first. The crabs move sideways, pincers up, some sinking back into rocky soil-sand, still clambering to flee. The ground crawls with tiny jointed legs.

Paco imitates the baby crabs, scampering sideways, laughing from his belly. He stoops down and turns over some more rocks along the way. Looking back every few feet he calls big his brother, "Segundo! Hurry up!"

Segundo peers into the miniscule black holes, pressing both hands flat on the ground. Water seeps into his pants, soaking his knees—a shadow moving up his thighs.

"Wait!"

Lured by the shiny rock crabs, Segundo and Paco stay too long. Night is falling. A high concentration of luminescent phytoplankton and comb jellies are lighting up the river's surface, and all along the edge.

"In the water—"

"I see them."

"Make them light up. More. Look." Segundo shows Paco by running his hand along the surface of the river—back and forth, back and forth—raking his fingers through the jellies whose bodies are mostly invisible, detectable only by their light. Paco imitates his brother and dips his hand in.

"THEY'RE GLOWING, SEGUNDO. They're GLOWING," Paco exclaims with pure glee and lifts both hands, cupping so many comb jellies they stream over his thumbs and fall back into the water, making the surface shimmer more with each widening ripple. He dips them back in and raises his cupped palms until his fingertips touch Segundo's. Segundo catches the luminous stream passing from Paco's hands to his.

The apartment is on the ground level and has a small terrace with four wicker chairs set around a small wrought iron table. His sister Glenny occupies one of the chairs. She is writing in a composition notebook, with her swan neck bent forward.

Segundo runs past her into the apartment.

He sees only black and grey contours when he enters, taking the hallway on the left to the last bedroom door, which is on the far right. He shuts the door and heads straight to the corner where his mother keeps the altar; every saint behind glass. Baby Jesus, the Virgin Mary, Saint Martin, Saint Francis of Assisi, crucified Christ all in color standing beside a tall glass of water and a dessert dish with Paco's favorite candy. Segundo sits on the floor gazing at the candy's glossy wrappers. He does not move until Glenny calls him.

"Come eat right now, Segundo!" Her voice is a screech.

He can still smell the chick on his hands, something like cornmeal and sweat.

"Hurry up, I don't want to hear anything from mami."

"I get a bottle?"

"Let's go! You have to eat before she gets here."

Thirty minutes later, Segundo still has not touched his hardboiled egg. He bites off a piece of bread. Bits slide out over his bottom lip as he chews with his mouth open. He places bits of bread on the edge of his plate with wet fingers.

Glenny puts down her fork with a little clatter.

"You want?"

"You're impossible! Stop that. It's disgusting!"

"Eating?"

"What twelve-year-old still needs a bib?"

"A what?"

"Instead of that Batman mask you want, I'm telling ma to buy you bibs labeled with day of the week—Monday, Tuesday, Wednesday. You think you can keep them straight?"

"Your mask?"

"Could you act normal?"

Spittle and food slip out of his mouth, followed by smacking sounds.

“And can you put your tongue back in your head?”

Segundo cowers in his chair.

“I mean, is there anyone worse than you?” Glenny says. “First, you’re born. And second, that face—”

“I’m second?”

“Come here. Let me tell you something."

Segundo shakes his head.

“Now you don’t like secrets, you nasty?”

But Segundo knows her habits—what she does with her loose hands. Mean backhand, hers.

“I wanna see if you can finally understand. You wanna know what’s wrong with you, half-born?” She leans over the table laying both hands flat on it.

Segundo leans back as she brings her face closer to his.

“Half-born understand?” Segundo parrots.

"Listen, it’s not about being good, or bad like with that thing you did to Paco. It’s what I’ve told you every single day of your entire life. The same thing the block tells you when you want to play and they don’t, and then you go become a garbage collector.”

"What?! What is it?"

"That. You. Are. Fucking. Ugly. GUÁCALA."

Cold

Naima Coster

The cold is a thing any woman can grow accustomed to. Lacey May learned how in precisely three days, which was quicker than anyone who knew her would have ever expected.

It was a Wednesday, newly November, and she was raking the leaves in the front yard, when it occurred to her to check the gas tank. Her knuckles were red and sore from the few minutes she had been outside, and it wouldn't be long before the nights started to dip toward the thirties. The tank was shaped like a tiny submarine, and it stood in the shadow of the house. She pulled up the metal lid and saw the needle on the gauge pointing down to fifteen percent. Lacey ran inside, still holding the rake, and she dropped the heat down as low as she could stand.

She passed the rest of the day in her good coat, the one Robbie bought her the winter she was pregnant with their first. It was big on her now, but she was more or less fine with it on. She kept the kettle boiling because the steam felt good rising on her face while she stood at the stove, and if she drank cup after cup of coffee, she could keep her hands warm, too. By noon, she was shaking from all the caffeine, her fingernails tinged with blue. She wanted Robbie to call so she could tell him about the tank and ask how long fifteen percent would last, but he didn't. She called the agency instead to ask again if they'd found anything for her yet.

"It's kinda hard when you haven't worked in ten years. And all you've ever done is fry fries." The receptionist spoke slowly, as if she didn't expect Lacey to understand.

"I've been raising my girls," Lacey said.

"I mean real work, out of the house. Employment."

"I'm pretty sure I could answer the phone."

"You don't have any qualifications."

Lacey wanted to hang up on her, or to insult her again, but the receptionist didn't seem interested in a fight. Besides, she shouldn't risk ticking off the woman who could decide whether to move her folder down to the bottom of the pile. So Lacey mentioned how she had earned decent grades in high school, was quick in the kitchen, better behind the wheel than most.

"You can write that down if you want," she said, and the receptionist was quiet for a long while. Finally, she said she would add a note to Lacey's file and give her a call if anything opened up. Lacey thanked the woman for her time and got off the phone.

Later on, when she heard the school bus turn up the road, Lacey climbed into the crawlspace and hauled down the old duffel bag filled with the children's winter clothes. She waited at the door for them, her arms loaded down with woolen things that smelled of dust and damp, from months spent shut up in the dark. The girls blazed in, chattering, their cheeks windblown, and Lacey handed them each an extra sweater and a pair of mittens, a scarf for Margarita.

"It's winter in our house!" she said, and the girls caught on quickly. They dropped their school bags and swathed themselves in the new layers, made a big noise stomping around the living room. Soon they were all explorers, sliding across a stretch of ice in Alaska. Somehow, Lacey became a sled, and the girls scrambled on top of her, and, although she couldn't move, it made them laugh. Diane pretended to be a dog, one of those racing wolf dogs, so she got down on all fours and howled, which made their real dog Jenkins dart behind the couch to hide.

They kept on their sweaters and scarves while they cooked grilled cheese, the yellow squares gobbled up by their hands faster than Lacey could set them in the pan. They were pleased when they were all allowed to lie down in bed with Lacey, and she didn't make them crawl out from under the blankets to wash their greasy fingers or their unbrushed teeth. Jenkins dozed beneath them on the floor, as if he couldn't feel the cold at all, and the girls watched their breath puff overhead.

"That's oxygen," Lacey said. "It's what we breathe. You spell it O-X-Y—"

Her oldest, Noelle, liked to look at picture books about the ocean and outer space. In the summer, she tended to the tomato plants in the yard and caught dragonflies and burned their wings off under her magnifying glass. She could be a scientist one day, if she started her extra learning now. Lacey was spelling for her.

Noelle looked a lot older than almost-ten, the little swipes of purple under her eyes a reminder that no matter how fine they all seemed, the girls missed their daddy. She repeated after Lacey, a blanket tucked under her chin, and her face serious, as if she knew how much every letter was worth.

"G-E-N." Diane and Margarita gave a little round of applause when their sister got it right.

The next morning the girls went off to school, all of them with pink noses and runny eyes. Lacey saw them down the hill, and she was jealous of their little black heads disappearing into the bus. They were off to somewhere the thermostat was set much higher than fifty-five.

She took a shower to beat the cold, and it was the most pleasure she had felt since Robbie went away. Had water always been this warm? The stream of it so steady and mighty and good? Her hands set to work on every inch of her—her elbows, her neck, the insides of her thighs—and the heat seemed to sink in deep, underneath the top layer of skin—what was it called? The epidermis?— she had learned the name in high school. It was only these last few weeks, since the nurse moved in next door, that Lacey started remembering she hadn't been half bad at biology. She had seen the nurse driving down the road to third shift at the hospital and thought, *I could have been you.* Sure, the nurse was fat and had no husband and left her boy with a babysitter overnight and didn't bother with the leaves in the yard, but it was probably seventy, seventy-five degrees over in her bungalow, and wasn't that worth something?

After the shower, Lacey felt the sin of her wet hair. It made the cold worse, a new chill dripping on her neck and shoulders, so she wrapped her head in towels. How much gas was she using now? How many percents did it take to heat the house every day? She wondered whether to go out and check the tank again, but she decided against it. She couldn't have been using that much, not when it was only fifteen degrees warmer inside than out.

Lacey opened all the curtains to let in the sunshine, thinking some light might warm the place. Half an hour later, she went around drawing them all closed because maybe she was letting in a draft. She had lived in the house for four years, ever since Robbie's promotion at the shop, and still she didn't know how it all worked. When she took off her robe to get dressed, she had a sudden, terrible thought: How did the water get heated? Did that use up the gas, too?

She didn't want to call her sister-in-law but she did. There was nothing else to do.

"I'm worried it might be bad for the girls. All this cold. And the next check doesn't come for another two weeks."

"Why don't you sell your food stamps?"

"Cause we got to eat, Annette."

"Well, the cold never killed nobody. When we were kids, it was always cold in our house. And I turned out just fine. And we can't blame the cold for Robbie—"

"It's not his fault, Annette. I've told you. He's got—" Lacey searched for the words, tried to remember the doctor's exact phrase. "A chemical unbalanced."

"I told you to get a job. I said it a year ago when he started disappearing."

"I thought he was getting better."

"And I told him not to buy that house, that one day the mortgage would get him. Nothing in this life is free, least of all houses. You played dumb for too long, Lacey May."

"Why don't you come by and see how cold it is for yourself? All we need is a little loan."

"No ma'am," Annette said. "Robbie already cleaned me out, remember?"

Lacey started to cry. Her sister-in-law tried to calm her but it was no use.

"How'd you burn through the last check so quick anyway? It's only the middle of the month."

When Lacey didn't say anything, Annette made sense of her silence and cursed.

"You're as shit-rotten as he is," she said. "You don't love those little girls half as much as they deserve."

Lacey put herself to bed, her hair leaking all over the pillows. The dog followed her into the room, whimpering, and settled on the floor by her side. She drew three blankets up over herself and started talking out loud. It was like she was praying, only she was talking to Robbie.

Why'd you buy me this house if it was going to be so cold? Why'd you buy me this house if you was going to leave me alone?

It had been good for a long time. All through Noelle and Diane being babies, and the first years of Margarita's life, they had lived in town. They had less, but it was fine. Then they bought this little house, blue with white shutters, at the top of the hill on a patch of cleared land. There were only two other houses out in these woods. The first had been empty for a year, after the last family moved closer to town, and the other belonged now to that nurse and her kid. Before, their neighbors had been the Kings, an old couple that took afternoon coffee out on the porch. They died within a few weeks of each other, both in the spring, in their sleep, which Lacey thought was the best kind of ending you could ever expect from life.

Their house was drafty and small, all wood except for the concrete porch that wrapped all around, which Robbie had built himself. There were swings out back for the girls, a plastic slide Diane and Noelle had outgrown but that Margarita still liked to climb.

When he was all right, they would go out to the back porch and drink beers after the girls had gone to sleep. If they drank too much, he would fuck her right there on the porch, Lacey down on all fours, the concrete scraping her knees. *This is freedom*, he would say. *I can fuck my wife under a sky full of stars, if I want.* There was no one around, not in this dark, these twenty miles from town, and he could slap her rump and pull her hair, and she could bite down hard on his finger, and Lacey wanted it all, how he handled her, how it could feel like they did not just own the house, but the whole hill, and the woods, their own skin, one another.

Those were the only times he was rough—he'd never hit her, or the girls, not even after he got real bad. He would get mean and he would cry and he would scream, but he never raised his hand. Only if she asked him, only if they were out on the porch, and it was just a part of their way, as good a feeling as his nimble cock poking at the inside parts that made her sing.

It wasn't that he had stopped loving her, no, and he hadn't stopped loving the girls. The unbalance in his brain came first, and then the drugs. And once he had the drugs, his brain needed more, and he started doing things and disappearing so he could have more. It was like being sick. She hadn't made it all up to defend him—the lawyer had shown her papers, a diagnosis, to prove it was true. But when she told Annette, all Annette had said was, "You're planning on telling that to a judge?"

Lacey was all out of tears in a while, and she was shivering under those blankets, as cold as if she weren't inside a house at all. She got up and found the coin jar under the sink. She had been filling it back up ever since Robbie left. It was mostly pennies. She gave Jenkins a pat goodbye and carried the jar out to the car. She drove downhill along the service road to the store. Inside she found a clerk and asked for Hank, and she waited for him by the coin machine, trading in all her pennies for a flimsy receipt that explained she had earned nine dollars. Hank surfaced from one of the aisles in blue jeans and a pretty yellow workers' vest. His hair was long and combed over so it hung down one side of his face. He waved her out the sliding doors and into the parking lot, where he kissed her behind the ear and lit a cigarette to hear her out. He didn't offer her one.

She explained about the fifteen percent, and how she still had stamps for food, and she had paid the mortgage, and she had been careful and budgeted for everything, everything except the gas. It hadn't gotten cold yet since Robbie went away. She didn't know.

"God, Lacey, you're as pretty as you ever were. Do you know that? Your teeth are fit to eat."

Lacey had hardly felt beautiful at all these days; her eyes were red from too little sleep, and she hadn't been able to afford her good shampoo in weeks. But she did still have her smile, at least. She looked at Hank and turned it on.

"You ever think about selling that house?"

"Robbie wouldn't like that. It's the only thing we got to pass down to the girls."

'Well, you're not going to be able to pass down anything if they freeze to death."

"Can you bring me on to work or not?"

Hank finally tapped a cigarette out of the pack and handed it to her. She bent over the lighter in his hands, and when she straightened up, she saw he was staring at her. She blew the smoke out in his direction. They had been teenagers together, all three of them, her and Hank and Robbie, when they were all in high school and working at the Hot Wing. Hank had a face full of acne then but it had cleared now to nothing but scars, dark shadows along his cheeks. He didn't look half bad anymore, with his braces off, his hair washed clean. He had always wanted her, she knew, and she had liked having him get things off a high shelf for her, or rush over with a washcloth if she burned herself on the oil. But Robbie was the one who had won her. They had all stayed friends for a while, until the girls came and they moved out of town, and forgot all about Hank until they came in to do their shopping with the girls, and he would nod at them, and they would ask after his mother, and he would look down at his walkie-talkie and wait for someone to call for him, to request a manager in an aisle on the other end of the store.

"You know I got a place?"

Hank sucked on the tip of his cigarette and let it dance between his lips.

"I've got a yard and everything. You and your girls would fill it right up."

"You would do that for us? You've got an extra room?"

"I've got a pullout in the basement."

"It would be tight, all four of us on the couch, but it's better than letting the girls freeze—"

Hank laughed and shook his head.

"Lacey May, you never could take a hint."

Lacey tilted her head and looked at him confused.

"Let's put it this way—if you stayed with me, it wouldn't cost you nothing, but it wouldn't be free neither."

The wind blew hard and kicked up the smell of gasoline from the pump at the edge of the lot. Lacey noticed she hardly felt the cold, her skin slowly getting used to the chill, but she pulled her coat around her anyway.

"How would I explain that to the girls?" she said. "They think their father's on the coast, working a fishing job."

Hank shrugged. "I'm a man, not a saint, Lacey."

She stared at the white button on his vest: TEAM LEADER. Until now she had never believed the stories she had heard about him. The rumor was that he was so lonesome he had started taking the high school girls who stocked the aisles out to the back lot during his breaks. He gave them overtime and the shifts they wanted if they let him fondle their tits for a while. It wasn't the worst thing she'd ever known a man to do, but she wouldn't have pinned it on a man like Hank.

"I think I'll go inside and get a few things for the girls," Lacey said. She stepped around him and walked toward the store.

"You were always too proud, Lacey May."

When she didn't turn around, Hank called after her again.

"You made the wrong choice!"

This time Lacey hollered back.

"I told you it's not his fault! It's his brain!"

With her nine dollars, Lacey bought a tin of coffee, another block of cheese, a magazine about TV stars and their weddings, and a fistful of bubblegum lollipops for the girls. She drove back with the heat on low, but still she felt like she was suffocating, so she rolled down all the windows. It was as if she missed the cold. She let the frosty air whip around her, even if she might regret it later, even if she'd have to fight the temptation later on to go sit in the car and let the engine run.

When the girls clattered in after school, Lacey gave them each a lollipop, and Diane, who had prematurely lost three baby molars to cavities, looked at her mother, as if to see if she were sure. Lacey nodded at her and said, "That's right, sweetheart. Go ahead, let it rot your teeth."

She asked the girls to tell her what they had learned in school while she made their sandwiches and mixed chocolate powder into hot milk. Diane and Margarita huddled under a blanket on the floor, Jenkins weaseling his way underneath. Noelle sliced up the cheese into perfect thin squares.

"You could perform surgery with those hands," Lacey said. "Gifted hands!" She knew she'd heard the phrase somewhere but she couldn't remember exactly where. Noelle didn't seem to be touched by the compliment and didn't look up from the cutting board as she pushed the knife through the brick of cheese.

"How come Daddy doesn't come back on the weekends? We've been to the beach—it's not that long a drive."

Lacey gave her a little tap on the nose. "Cause that's when they catch the biggest fish— something about the tide. When he calls, I'll have him explain it."

They ate on the couch, the plates on their laps, their hands over their blankets, Jenkins's fur starting to knot into the fibers of the wool.

"Is it still winter in our house?" Margarita asked, and Lacey kissed the top of her head.

"Yes, ma'am. Isn't it fun?" She turned on the TV.

They watched a cop show, and the girls didn't mention their father. They didn't notice Lacey look away when the officers caught up to the burglar. They wrestled him down onto the shoulder of the highway. They knocked his head against the grass.

The phone rang, and Lacey leapt up. It was Robbie! He'd finally gotten the money she put in his commissary, and he was placing a call. It would all be worth it—heat or no heat, the girls would hear their father's voice, they'd remember they had a father, and that he hadn't wanted to leave.

The phone was painfully cold to her ear and Lacey waited for the operator's voice to come through, for her chance to press a button and choose to accept a call from a county inmate.

"Miss Ventura," said a bland voice. It was the receptionist from yesterday.

"Yes, this is Mrs. Ventura."

She waited to hear they'd found her a job, maybe in a laundromat, selling those tiny bottles of detergent to people who had forgotten theirs, or maybe even a doctor's office where she could put away supplies, label the samples of pee, point people to the bathroom. She would smile and give directions like, "Yes, ma'am, make a left at the end of the hall." She had a good manner—her boss at the Hot Wing had told her so—and she had her smile. Most of all, she wasn't stupid. There was plenty she could learn to do.

"Mrs. Ventura, the check you gave us with your application bounced. We can't process any of the paperwork until you write us a new one—and refund us the thirty dollars we got charged for your bad check."

"I had the money when I first wrote the check. Why'd you wait so long to cash it?"

Lacey didn't hear the receptionist's answer because Margarita had started to cry.

"Mommy, I'm so cold. Why is it so cold?" she said.

"Cause Daddy's fishing," Noelle said, shaking her head. "Cause he left us. Didn't he leave us? He doesn't want us anymore."

Lacey dropped the phone and slapped her child. When Noelle started shouting, Diane joined in, saying they shouldn't fight, so Lacey slapped her too, and Margarita for good measure, and sent them all to their room. When she picked up the phone, the receptionist wasn't on the line. She could hear Margarita in the bedroom, still crying about the cold. They would be warmer if they all gathered in her bed—she knew that—but she let them cry softly into the dark. She had been stuck with the cold for two days and they were carrying on as if the heat weren't on at all. When the girls were quiet, whether because they fell asleep or gave up on crying, she stood and turned the temperature up five degrees.

She hadn't wanted to send the last of the government check to Robbie, but he needed all kinds of things: new underwear and cups of instant soup because the meals they served inside were rotten. He was clean and seeing a doctor who gave him pills that helped, so she did the math and then deposited the money. He had promised to save some of the money to call.

In the night she went to check on the girls. She stuck their little feet underneath the blankets, sealed the covers around their skinny bodies like cocoons. It was easier for them. They weren't around all day. They only sensed his absence in the few hours before bed—Lacey never got away from it.

Diane woke with a fever. She was eating her cereal too slowly, and when Lacey touched her hand to the girl's forehead, her skin was burning up. Noelle put her hand on her hip and stood up from the table. "You did this," she said. "This is all your fault."

And Margarita chimed in, "When's Daddy coming? When Daddy's here, it never gets so cold."

"It's sixty degrees in here!" Lacey screamed. "That's the temperature right now in California!" She had made up the fact, but it sounded true. What did they know? When they were home, they were under blankets, and sixty degrees wasn't bad for such short whiles—it took hours for the cold to snake into your bones. It had started to happen to her. She had risen with a pain in her knee, a stiff back, as if, in two days, the cold had managed to make her old. She started yelling at the children that they were spoiled, that they were off to school where it was warm while she had to stay behind.

"Well it's Friday now!" Noelle shouted. "What's going to happen on the weekend?"

And while Noelle yelled at her, and Margarita started moaning about her daddy and a tingling in her fingers and toes, Diane vomited on the kitchen floor. Jenkins started to lap it up, and Lacey kicked him hard.

The girls nearly missed the bus, and Lacey had to chase it down in her slippers and her robe. The only girl who kissed her good-bye was sick little Diane, her face crimson, her hair sticking to her face with sweat. She had to have the heat on by the time the girls came back. She was determined.

On her walk up the hill, Lacey couldn't understand how tired she felt. Ever since they took Robbie away, her days were emptier, as if he had been the one she stayed at home to raise. Part of it was autumn—there was nothing to do in the yard, no vegetables to water or uproot, no grass to cut. The house was clean, the girls gone. There was hardly any cooking to do without Robbie's paycheck—no chickens to roast, or turnips, no beef to bread and fry. She couldn't spend a day making sandwiches, slathering government mayonnaise on bread, waiting for the cheese to get slippery and hot. And there was no more of the sweet waiting—for him to call between fixing up cars to see how her day was, or to apologize for the scene he'd made last night and say he didn't remember, no more running to meet him at the door, his clothes thick with the smell of paint thinner, sweat, and other men.

Lacey went to the shed for her rake and shears, then she walked across a quarter acre of woods to knock on the door of the fat, unmarried nurse. Lacey read the name on the mailbox—Amelia Green. She started rehearsing the lines in her head. *If you'd be so kind, Miss Amelia.*

It was a while before the door opened, and Amelia stood in a checkered pajama set, fleshy and tall, her hair in a big wet knot on top of her head. Lacey could feel the heat streaming out the open door, and it seemed to overtake the cold outside to touch her fingertips, her frozen nose, and her lips, which she hadn't realized were cracked. She was embarrassed, but she smiled her smile anyway.

"I wanted to see if I could help clear up your yard."

Amelia Green stared at her as if she had no teeth at all.

"You know, prune back the bushes and pull up the weeds, rake the leaves. I could wash your car too. The front steps." The gutters could use a cleaning, as well, or she could sweep up the leaves covering the porch. If Miss Amelia had a ladder, she could even clear the roof.

She realized then she should have changed out of her robe and slippers. She could have put on her good blue blouse. Her boots. She could have dressed herself like a woman who worked.

Amelia Green clucked her tongue.

"Why would I pay you to clean up this yard when it's gonna be covered up in ice in a few weeks?"

Lacey wondered whether to tell her about Robbie, whether this nurse, whose lights were always on, whose house was warm, who had a babysitter drive up through the woods to watch her boy while she went to the hospital to draw blood or clear bedpans or take temperatures or whatever it was she did, could ever understand what it was to have a husband, to love him with your bones.

"My propane is down to fifteen percent. Probably ten now."

"That'll last you till Monday when the truck comes around. You need their number?"

Lacey explained her middle girl had a fever; her youngest was only six. They were making out all right with Robbie gone—it was just the heat.

"What I'm trying to say is, I ain't got it, and I don't know what else to do."

Amelia crossed her arms. "You see, the rest of us, we work. We don't depend on the government or no husband."

"Maybe you could just lend me a few gallons out of your tank to hold us over."

"If you expect me to pity you, I don't. You're not the only one who married some sonofabitch who can't take care of his own kids—"

"It's not his fault. He's got a chemical unbalance—"

"They all do," Amelia said, and she went to close the door.

Lacey pushed her hand against the frame.

"My babies are freezing."

"This is real life, sweetheart. Find a way—that's what women do."

"You fat cunt."

The nurse slammed the door.

Lacey stomped through the woods, smashing down fallen branches and the still-green grass under her slippers. When she got near the house, she could hear her phone was ringing. She ran to make it in time.

"Robbie?"

It was the school nurse. Diane had vomited again on the bus, and she needed to go home. Could Lacey come and pick her up? On the long drive to the school, Lacey found herself shaking. When she went to the office and gave her name, they sent her straight to the principal's office.

Margarita was the one who had spilled the beans. When her teacher asked her why she kept putting her head down on her desk, she said she hadn't slept right because it was winter in her house. And since Diane threw up on the bus, it wasn't hard to put two and two together.

"I'm working on a solution," Lacey said.

The principal shook her head and asked what was going on—wasn't her husband a mechanic at the body shop off Haw? Lacey hadn't realized that they didn't know. Shouldn't there have been a letter that got sent from the court or the jail to the school? Wasn't there something the government had done to spare her this moment?

"My husband got high and stole a cop car. Not one of the black and white sheriff's ones, a regular one. It just belonged to a cop. It was parked in front of a bar downtown. He didn't know."

The principal said she was sorry, but she couldn't look the other way. Lacey said she knew she wasn't the only one to ever have to lower the heat, one November or another, but the principal didn't back down.

"I'm sorry, Mrs. Ventura, but after Monday, I'll have to make a call. You've got the weekend."

Lacey went around to the classrooms and got all her girls. They drove home in silence, past the houses all in a row, and then out of town to where it was all fields and forgotten barns, the railroad tracks where they had to stop and wait for a train to pass.

"Woo-woo!" sang Margarita and it made Diane smile weakly, her cheeks pink.

Back at home, she boiled cans of broth for the girls, peeled and dropped in potatoes, a tin of shredded chicken. And then she made grilled cheeses too and chocolate milk and they carried it all into Lacey's bed, where she piled blankets on top of the girls and then crawled in herself.

"If one of us is going to be sick, we might as well all be sick together," she said, and she kissed her girls on the nose. It was still light out, hardly past midday.

"Aren't you going to turn up the heat? You heard what the principal said."

Noelle still wasn't looking at her, her ears flushed bright, and Lacey wondered whether she was catching a fever too, or if she was just ashamed. Maybe her friends at school knew now how they had been living.

"Hush," Lacey said. "I'm going to tell y'all a story."

The girls squeezed in closer to their mother, even Noelle, although she probably only wanted to get warm.

"Once upon a time, there was a princess, and she lived in a castle deep in a forest. And she lived there with her sisters, but there was no one else around cause all the men were at war. It was a kingdom with no old people, you see, so there was no one to show them what to do while the men was gone. How to fill the moat, how to feed the horses, how to keep the torches lit, and the dungeons clean—"

"What's a moat?" Diane asked, sucking on a Tylenol and making a face. Lacey told her to swallow it.

"So they saddled up the horses, and they went riding, far and far, over valleys and streams to a kingdom they had heard of where all the men went to war and never came back. The princesses in this kingdom showed them how to do all the things they were afraid of—how to clean the stables and grow wheat, how to cast spells, and burn the dead—"

"How to fill the moat?"

"Mmhm—and when they knew everything they needed to know, they went riding back to their kingdom, all day, and all night, and when they got there, they weren't afraid anymore. They were all ready to rule, but they didn't have to after all, cause while they were gone, the princes had all come home. They had won the war."

Diane asked whether they had a party, and Lacey explained they hadn't just held parties but weddings. One wedding every day, one for each princess and her prince.

"And they feasted and they drank and they ate chocolate cake, and when the moon came up, they would go out on boats and talk about how it felt like there never wasn't any war at all."

Noelle rolled her eyes. "Short war," she said.

"I like that story!" Margarita shouted. Lacey told her to lower her voice.

"I hate it. It's stupid," Noelle said, and she crossed her arms. "They ride their horses all that way to another kingdom and they learn all those things, and it doesn't even matter. They never even get a chance to rule."

Lacey wanted to explain that at least they knew how, and you should never give up a prince if the prince really loves you, but Noelle plugged up her ears, and Margarita shouted that she wanted to be princess, and Diane stood solemnly and asked for someone to go with her to the bathroom because she had to throw up.

After the girls nodded off, Lacey slipped out from under the blankets to clean up the bowls and the mugs they had left on the floor. She shut off the light and went out to the back porch with one of the leftover lollipops from the supermarket. She sucked it down to the white stick, cracking the hard candy between her front teeth. She counted the days on her fingers since she had sent Robbie the money—five—and he still hadn't called. *Goddamn you, Robbie,* she thought. *Goddamn.*

She went back inside, and she didn't feel a difference anymore between inside and out. Maybe it wouldn't matter for her anymore, whether the heat was high or low or off. She wouldn't be able to shake off the chill for a while—it was under her skin now. But the girls.

Lacey found her old address book in a drawer, and she went flipping through the pages until she found him there, alphabetized by last name. *Sommer, Hank*. She carried the address book and the phone out to the living room. She muted the TV and dialed, waited for the ringing to stop.

"I knew you'd change your mind," he said, and Lacey smiled. With her free hand, she turned up the thermostat a full ten degrees.

from FEARFUL SYMMETRY

Ansel Elkins

Trap Hill, N.C. May 1842

CHANG	ENG
Outside my window	Sound of splitting beech wood is our
tulip trees awaken	only correspondence.
and burst. *Adelaide.*	You heave the axe
By day we clear-cut our acreage, an	with vigor, more vehement
inescapable aroma	with each stroke.
of split green wood. Dis-	
cord of spring brings me bitterness	The sap in you is rising.
even as the bees wildly	
court the fruit trees.	
Ripen, I ask, ripen me.	I, too
	feel these hundred acres summoned
This land longs for only one thing:	to virile green. Vines muscular and
to be seeded. I begin	obscene
	coil heated arms around the barn.
to hate him. We split fire-	You drive your whipped mule,
wood. The axe	cut the plough deep into
is an instrument of joy.	this begging field.
How the wood loves to be released	

from itself. I ask God to knife
us into cleanly halved
men. Sever me
at the green stem
of our sternum. Halve
us from each other so that I
may have my own
bride.

Each blow of the hatchet
measures your desire to make a wife of
her. She unties
the endless night
of her hair, combs herself
before the mirror, frees
the long tight braid with a single stroke
of the comb's teeth.

Everywhere, Signs

Anita Felicelli

The answer for me back then was yes—most numbers vibrated. They vibrated in Pittsburgh, they vibrated in Chennai, and the sense that I was deeply connected to everything in the world by numbers was infinitely comforting to me. My toes quivered when Miss Wabash—despised by the other fifth graders for her strictness—teased out these reverberations in purple chalk during the math hour. Amma, noticing how much I loved numbers, had asked Miss Wabash to give me extra math worksheets, even though it was not computation that thrilled me, but the numbers themselves—the accounting of all that was domestic or wild, safe or dangerous, a kind of language that remained stable no matter the city. I faithfully tallied the number of fruit jelly candies Amma bought at the green grocer's, the number of perforated ceiling tiles in my father's office, the number of thrushes sipping from the bird bath by my classroom, the number of former friends that called me a terrorist in the months after 9/11.

The trouble began during our annual three-week winter trip to Chennai in 2001, just a few days before we returned home. The prospect of returning to Pittsburgh filled me with dread, even though this time my grandfather was coming to live with us because his heart condition was worsening. We were staying at his small, sparely furnished two-bedroom flat with its orange and white tile floors and pit toilet. Thatha was a retired mathematics professor and the beige walls were lined with overflowing bookshelves. It was a Friday with no cosmic significance according to the numerology book I'd convinced my mother to buy that morning. Yet it remained seared in my memory because for many years afterwards, my mind worried over how easily everything could have gone differently. If only they had.

After lunch, I'd read the frontispiece of the numerology book: an optimistic promise that inside were answers about why there was so much chaos in the world. I finished calculating my family's karmic numbers according to the instructions, and then I'd laid out all of Thatha's heart pills on the dresser and counted them. Sixty-one. When I was done counting, I gathered the pills and rearranged them in their five respective bottles. I wandered out to the narrow cul-de-sac in front of my grandfather's stucco split-level. On the porch, my grandfather was smoking a cigar while my mother scolded him for not taking care of his health in a blend of Tamil and English. "You're doing this to yourself," she said. Thatha rubbed his swollen legs under his veshti. I didn't like how shrill Amma's voice got when she spoke to my grandfather, and tried to hurry past them with my book in hand.

"Put that rubbish book away," my grandfather called after me. I pretended I didn't hear him, although he continued chastising my mother for buying the book as I walked into the cul-de-sac.

Pot-bellied clouds, the grey of gunshot, rolled overhead, signaling an impending monsoon. Up the street, near the busy intersection, idle young men chewing betel leaves hovered on the sidewalk and cattle lumbered alongside nimble yellow rickshaws and bulky motorcyclists and honking cars. In the other direction, housewives squatted in front of their houses drawing elaborate kollam with white, pink and green chalk. The neighborhood kids chased each other screaming and laughing, and for a moment, I wished I was among them. My old friends from the convent school had returned to the classroom after Christmas, so I'd tried to play with the neighborhood kids, but my accent had changed in the three years since we'd moved to the States, and they'd mocked me. It was not as painful as my life in Pittsburgh, where the kids teased me about the veil of downy hairs on my upper lips and arms, and shunned me because my mother packed me lunches of rice and sambar in a steel tiffin every day. Some of the girls had told me sambar was the grossest thing they had ever smelled or seen someone eat. Often, one of the boys would grab the tiffin tin and throw it away, leaving me to fish through the trash for the tin so I wouldn't have to explain to my mother why I'd come home without it.

Next door were our family friends, the Kumaraswamys, who we'd known well before we moved to Pittsburgh three years before. Through the crisscrossed black metal bars of their front gate, I saw Latha Kumaraswamy sitting with her toddler in the dimly lit room, listening to the Rolling Stones' "Sympathy for the Devil."

I called through a diamond-shaped opening.

Latha unlatched the heavy gate and tugged it open. "What do you need, Hagar kutty?"

I asked for her birthdate, explaining about the numerology book, its practical magic, and how much it seemed to explain. She sniffed. "We don't believe in that kind of superstitious nonsense," she said, but invited me in for tea.

In the sitting area, an army of porcelain animal figurines looked out from the curiosity cabinet. Anju placed a doll's cup in front of me. "Paal venuma?" I nodded and she poured milk into the cup.

Latha said, "Tell me about America, Hagar." As I talked, she smiled, not in the condescending way that adults did when they thought they'd made headway with a recalcitrant youngster, but as if she were genuinely interested. "And do you like your school?"

I nodded, though what I really wanted to say was that I desperately missed my old friends, and I missed my grandfather. Latha continued asking questions—there was something exciting about being asked questions by a grown-up, as if I were an expert on America. "And the other children are nice to you?"

I hesitated a moment, and then I answered yes, as I knew my parents would want me to answer. In truth, just before our trip, Bobby Jamison had ambushed me in the cafeteria. He grabbed me by the shoulders and shoved me up against the concrete wall so that the back of my head banged against it and my teeth rattled. His freckles loomed so close to my face, I could smell the tuna fish on his hot breath and the gathering sweat under the brim of his backwards baseball cap. He pinned my wrists over my head, and squeezed them with such force he left painful, moon-shaped violet bruises. Beyond him, I saw the lunch lady, her hair wrapped in a net, watching from ten feet away. She did nothing. "Go back to Iraq," he yelled. I told him I was Indian. He spit at me, and let go of my wrists, and walked away without a backward glance. Afterward, I went to the girl's bathroom, curled up in the corner, and counted the tiny powder blue tiles on the floor until I could no longer see the beige grout between them, until they blurred into a sea. Miss Wabash rolled her eyes when I told her about the attack and said nobody likes a tattletale and boys would be boys.

The worst of it, though was not the bruises, but what had happened with Anne. Last year, Anne and I had slept over at each other's houses, French braided each other's hair, and played on the same handball team at lunch, and even on 9/11 when we learned of the nightmarish crashes of the airplanes, one of them in nearby Shanksville, we huddled together and whispered over our matching mauve ballerina lunchboxes. One day we were trading fruit roll-up flavors, and the next, silence. When my mother called out of concern, Anne's mother said Anne couldn't come to play dates at our house anymore. My mother's lips tensed after she told me, like she was keeping herself from saying something else, and when I asked her why, she only shrugged.

"Are you getting good grades?" Latha asked.

"Yes."

The commotion from the neighborhood children outside subsided as Latha's cook arrived to prepare dinner. Clanging pots, red chilies frying. The warm, comforting golden smell of ghee and cumin, the sound of mustard seeds sizzling. Latha would soon tell me it was time to return home. That's when it happened.

I dug my teeth into my lower lip, and said, "The teacher, she puts me in a garbage can."

"What?" Latha asked. She swung Anju onto her hip. "What are you talking about?"

"She makes me come inside during the lunch hour every week and forces me to stand inside a garbage can."

"What? In America? Truly?" Latha's eyes narrowed. "Are you making up a story? Hagar, it's wrong to make up stories."

"No, auntie, it's true! She thinks I'm a terrorist." I added, "I'm not a liar."

Latha slipped her feet into her black chappals. "Come, I'm going to walk you home." In that moment, I remembered the scolding my father had given me for being so sullen before we boarded the plane. *This is India, not the States, so smile and be pleasant*, my father had said, and what had I done instead? Made up an awful story. I was mindfully backpedaling, trying to come up with some way in which what I said was true.

"You don't have to walk me." I'd lit a match and given it to someone else to hold. What surprised me in that moment was that there were no signs I would lie, nor any that Latha would respond so strongly. It was December 28th. An odd number. A seven. It should have been a lovely day, like all odd days were, and it almost had been. I dragged my feet as we returned to my grandfather's house in the darkness and drizzle. Rain clouds obliterated the moon. The narrow street smelled like running mud and leaves. Above the neighbors' houses, the lanky palms shivered against strong gusts of wind.

"I want to talk to your mother," said Latha when we reached Thatha's gate. She forced her mouth into a smile, but the corners of her eyes stayed in place.

Inside, Amma sent me into the bedroom. Standing with an ear to the closed door, I could hear them firing back and forth in Tamil, my mother's voice rising both in pitch and volume, compared to Latha's hushed replies. Amma opened the door unexpectedly, knocking me back. Latha was gone. "You told her your teacher puts you in a garbage can? What is this?"

"Amma, she did. She hates me." Even after I'd done all her extra math problems correctly and quickly, Miss Wabash had said offhandedly that I was probably not going to be good enough at advanced mathematics to be a mathematician, and this statement alarmed me. In my convent school in Chennai, I had been at the top of the first, second and third standards. Most of what Miss Wabash taught in our Pittsburgh classroom, I had learned from my grandfather before starting school, but every time I raised my hand, she said, Oh my god, enough! Let somebody else answer.

"Miss Wabash wouldn't do that to you." Amma sounded desperate. "She gives you those extra math problems. I know you like those. On back-to-school night she was so welcoming. You're lying." Perhaps Amma was thinking of all the times over the last few months when she'd caught me stuffing cookies into my mouth because I'd missed lunch, hiding in the bathroom. I'd lied then, in spite of the crumbs around my mouth.

"I'm not lying!" I insisted, frantic now. "Why don't you believe me?"

I could imagine it so clearly, standing in the garbage can, my feet covered in five crumpled papers, two apple cores—one red and one green—the stink of half a tuna fish sandwich. "It happened over and over. And she makes me recite the times tables while I stand there. Because she thinks that I'm a show-off." Of course, it was freckle-faced Bobby Jamison and a band of boys who'd called me a show-off at lunchtime while making me recite the times tables, which I'd known for years, and mimicking my accent, but this fact was only a trivial detail now, as were the after school games of cops and robbers Bobby and I played after we arrived in the States. It seemed truer that it was Miss Wabash who never said anything when they teased me about my lunches, Miss Wabash who made me feel forgotten because she was in charge.

"I thought she was trying to help you with maths? You love numbers," Amma said. The rain pelted the windows.

"No, she just wanted to make fun of me," I said. I pushed away the memory of Miss Wabash recommending a novel about an Indian girl she thought I might like to get from the school library and the mixed feelings it stirred in me, both gratitude for the gesture and resentment that she assumed I'd only be interested in Indians. I plunked down on the hard cot in the living room where I slept, and flipped through my numerology book as the cook prepared dinner.

When my father returned from visiting his old classmates from IIT, I ran to hug him. As I wrapped my arms around his neck, Amma emerged from the kitchen and told him what Latha had said.

"The world has gone mad," Appa said. He pulled me from his neck and studied my face. "Is this true?"

I bit my lip. "Yes."

"No, I can't believe Miss Wabash could be so cruel," Amma said. "Americans know that Indians are not behind that attack."

"White people know no such thing. Anyone dark could be a terrorist in their minds. And at work, there's been a chill for the past few months. I've told you that."

Amma looked away, and then she said, "Well, that could be

anything. Maybe it's just a bad fit with the office."

I had heard them talking about the chill my father experienced at work before that night; although we'd all lived there the same amount of time, they saw two different Americas. Amma with her fawn-colored skin believed that the white graduate students saw her as their equal and that they made a place for her, while Appa with his blue-black skin was convinced that a number of white Americans in his program were racists who saw him as inferior. Later I would look back and realize I had taken something away from my mother that night—a confidence in the dream that brought us to America—and she never quite got it back again.

At the dinner table last night, Thatha asked, "Why these long faces?" He looked right at me.

I wasn't sure how to answer. My grandfather had criticized my parents over the last few nights, telling them they shouldn't have moved to the States, and that they should come home. Amma said, "We're just talking about how the world is a mess." Before she hid her face inside a teacup, I saw her blanche with anxiety.

Appa began talking quickly about the terrorist attack at the Parliament House in New Delhi. Later I would understand that this was so they could avoid getting another lecture from my grandfather. "We're discussing the suicide vest and these morons that blow themselves up for ideological reasons."

They commented on the rise of terrorism and violence in the world today, the clatter of their voices rising as they momentarily forgot about me and what I'd said. "You ignore the way America bullies other countries, the way it has supported fanatics for its own ends," my grandfather said. "No country deserves 9/11, but as Noam Chomsky said it is only in children's stories that power is used wisely to destroy evil. I'm not looking forward to living in a country like that."

"What would a professor of linguistics know about terrorism? And if you would take better care of your health, you wouldn't have to." Amma responded in irritation.

While mopping the spicy orange molaga podi with my dosa, I read the numerology book again. I brought the book with me when we went to have snacks and tea with my father's sister, and when we went to an older cousin's wedding on the penultimate day of our trip, but no matter how many times I reread the book, there seemed to be no numbers to explain my lie, or what would happen because of it.

***

We brought my grandfather back home with us when we returned to Pittsburgh. This was just days before the Indian government announced it would lay landmines along its border with Pakistan. In America, pundits were exploring who was to blame for missing all the signs that 9/11 would occur. We were detained longer than other passengers at customs in the airport, and I caught Appa looking at Amma, as if to say I told you so. "Where you coming from?" asked the rough-spoken blonde man at the counter. "No trips to the Middle East while you were there?" He dumped out the bags of clothes from the tailor's, my mother's turmeric creams and gold jewelry, the cowrie shell souvenirs they'd brought for friends, the sealed bags of seedai and jars of Latha's homemade lemon pickles. He searched thoroughly, and then we had to pack everything back in the bags, while the passengers behind us grumbled.

In front of our tiny rented house in Squirrel Hill, the pale January sky burned whiter than it had in Mandaveli, and my red plastic boots sank deep into the snow on the front lawn. I walked into the foyer and set my suitcase down. It looked exactly as we left it, furnished entirely by our American landlord because my parents were too busy working on their graduate degrees to make it look like it was ours. But the rooms smelled strange, like a doppelganger family had been living there in our absence, cooking their curries and burning their sandalwood incense.

"Very nice house, very nice," Thatha said in an impressed tone as he poked his head into the dining room. "But I am feeling a little faint." My mother helped Thatha settle in, and by next morning, when I woke up, the smell had vanished, or perhaps I'd grown used to it.

Usually my parents drove together to the university. But on that day, my mother called my school's principal. They parked in the school parking lot, my mother commenting on how dangerous it was that children were dropped off and picked up in such chaotic conditions. At the meeting with the principal my mother repeated what Miss Wabash had done and my father, zippered up in his stiff green winter jacket, watched the principal's face remain stiff and unmoved. When my mother spoke, it sounded like she was telling a true story about another girl who was being humiliated and I flooded with anger on her behalf.

"I'm sorry, but that's difficult to believe," said the principal after my mother stopped speaking. He rose from his seat and smiled at me. "Come now, Miss Wabash isn't cruel. She's new, but she's a very good teacher."

A faint pink flooded my mother's cheeks. "Hagar doesn't lie."

That was true, or at least it had once been true, which seemed like it could be the same thing. I hid my ice-cold hands in my pockets.

"There must be some misunderstanding," the principal said. "I'll investigate. I'll speak with Miss Wabash, but I'm sure this is some sort of mix-up or… exaggeration. We're in the midst of difficult times, as you know."

I said nothing. It was too late to say anything of significance. Amma paused, her face tightening like she didn't want to say what she said next. "It's not like we're Muslims."

"Do you want to take Hagar home for the day?" asked the principal.

My father had been silent the whole time, sizing up the principal—I had seen him do this in many other situations, erupt with anger after a few minutes of observing a person to see if he or she understood the moral gravity of a situation. I slouched deeper into my chair. "Miss Wabash should be suspended," he said suddenly. "Immediately."

"Afraid I can't do that," said the principal.

"She made my daughter feel like trash." Amma's voice was trembling, and my father put a hand on her sleeve. I had never seen my mother cry before.

Appa said, "If you don't discipline this teacher, we'll go to the press, to the School Board, to anybody who will listen to us."

The principal frowned and removed his wire-rimmed spectacles. He rubbed the scabby red skin under his glassy eyes and said, "Hagar, I'll ask you this once. I want you to tell me the truth now, hear? Is what your parents said true? Did Miss Wabash put you in a trashcan during the lunch hour? Did she call you a terrorist?"

"Yes," I whispered. "All true." I willed myself to cry to add much needed emphasis to what I was saying, but by now, I was too anxious, distracted by the need to survive, and my facial muscles wouldn't let loose any displays of emotion.

"All right. I will talk to Miss Wabash and if there's truth in what you're saying, I will suspend her. While I get to the bottom of this, we'll put Hagar in the other classroom."

After my parents left, the principal took me down the breezeway to the other classroom and whispered to the teacher. Thirty-one students stared at me. "Why are you in our class now?" asked a girl sitting next to me during social studies. I didn't answer.

"Terrorist," whispered a boy who'd built Lego castles with me after school two years before.

That day, I sat alone in the cafeteria rereading my numerology book, but the magic had already started to leech from the pages, and I felt nothing but dread. Picking at my rice, I noticed Miss Wabash, wearing a dazed expression as she glided down the breezeway towards the cafeteria with the principal. Her fine red hair was unspooling, slipping out of its clip. “I didn’t do anything to you, Hagar. You know that,” said Miss Wabash when they reached me.

“You did.”

“I know you’re having a hard time with the other kids. That’s why we work on those extra problems you love so much. I’m trying to help you. Why are you claiming I did something like that?”

“Nobody loves extra work.” I covered the book’s title with my hands and felt my front tooth sinking into my bottom lip. “You put me in the garbage can. You wanted me to be embarrassed.”

“I swear I didn’t do anything.” Miss Wabash turned to the principal, with her palms turned up. “She’s lying. Let me meet with her parents.”

When I returned home, Amma was waiting in the foyer. “Your teacher says she didn’t do it. They’re asking other students if they’ve seen anything.”

I shook my head. “She just doesn’t want to be punished."

“They’ll start the paperwork for your transfer to the other class in any case.” My mother went into the kitchen.

I thought she would come back and accuse me again, but instead she called my father and said that I was going through such a tough time, there was no way to force me to take back what I said. "Latha called to check on Hagar," Amma said. "I told her we don't know what will happen. Maybe my father is right. Maybe this isn't the right place for us." I wondered if we would move back to Chennai, into my grandfather's house. I'd see my friends at the convent school every day again. We'd be next door to the Kumaraswamys again.

Thatha came downstairs just then, walking slowly. He was holding a book of mathematical puzzles, and caught me standing just outside the kitchen door. "What are they saying?" he asked.

"Nothing," I said. "I was just counting the cracks in plaster." I pointed at the wall where a mysterious web of cracks spread.

"I count, too."

"You do?" I had never noticed him counting.

He beckoned me over to the dining room table, too far to eavesdrop any further on my parents. "I'll show you something else. Maybe it will help." He turned on the television, handed me a pencil, and opened the book to a puzzle, which he placed in front of me. Thinking about the difficult abstract problem took me away from Pittsburgh and all my troubles for a few moments. "See, isn't this better than that numerology book?"

But just then, on the television, a blonde anchor was talking about how war clouds loomed over India and Pakistan. Both countries were mobilizing their offensive army formations along the border and had conducted nuclear tests. "Secretary of State Colin Powell has issued a warning to Pakistan to rein in two militant Islamic organizations. The United States is trying to reduce tensions between these two hotheaded nations," she said.

"Hotheaded nations. Such condescension from the superior West. So rational! So righteous!" Thatha snorted. If my mother was with us when he went off on his tirades, she would tell him he shouldn't talk that way, and he would respond that there was no point in coddling children and I was smart enough to understand. I could hear the quiet hum of her voice—she was still on the telephone. "When it was convenient for Americans they allied themselves with militant Islam. Just to fight the Soviet Union. That's how these bloody fanatics have flourished."

A chill rippled through my body, as the blonde anchor kept talking in her easy, lukewarm voice about nuclear war and terrorists. Outside, snow fell in great white drifts, and the warm golden lights of the other houses were blurred. "Is there going to be a war?"

"Maybe."

"Where will we go?"

"If it's up to your parents, we'll stay right here," Thatha said. He rubbed his leg.

"Is it safe here?"

Thatha didn't answer. After a moment: "What I like about numbers is that they are eternal. People are the opposite. Inconsistent. Fickle. Things with people are always changing, and what's the right answer with people one moment is not the right answer the next. You can have faith in numbers. Here, let me explain the sultan's dowry problem to you."

***

Every student in Miss Wabash's fifth grade class was called to the principal's office that week to ask if they'd seen anything. At lunch on my second day back, Anne stared at me from across the cafeteria. She said something to the group of girls sitting with her, and then they all looked over with accusing expressions. It was the eighth of January. The book said eight had the worst vibrations. Eights were heavy karmic debt. That meant I had to accept whatever happened, swallow it whole as I had the truth. Outside the cafeteria, rain and snow battered the school. I ran out of the cafeteria and took shelter in a bathroom stall, waiting for lunch to be over, for the truth to come out.

On Thursday afternoon, the principal phoned Amma. They were not quite finished with the interviews, but the principal wanted all three of us to meet with Miss Wabash.

"Why are you agreeing to go?" Thatha said in a belligerent tone. By then, my parents had explained to him what was happening. "Why do you let these Americans push you around? You believe Hagar, don't you?"

"Of course we believe her."

"This is just how things are done here."

My parents looked at each other.

"We should move," Thatha said. "It's not safe for Hagar here."

On our way to meet the principal the following day, the car skidded on a patch of black ice in the residential neighborhood by the school. Appa struggled to regain control of the car, pumping the brakes as the vehicle careened towards the sidewalk. Nobody was on the road, and in a few moments, the tires found purchase, but we arrived at the principal's office badly shaken. Miss Wabash and the principal were already seated inside, talking.

The principal made small talk with my mother, who was trying to cover her agitation from our near-accident. After a few minutes, he said, “Three other students have said that Miss Wabash was inappropriate or tried to embarrass them, too. One said she made her stand in the corner the whole day. Another said she used the n-word around her.”

"I admit I may have, on the rare occasion, used excessive punishment," Miss Wabash said. She avoided making eye contact with my father or me, and looked straight at my mother instead. "I apologized to those students. But I didn't do what Hagar says I did." I felt amazement, believing that perhaps I was right to accuse Miss Wabash—she was guilty. If not of the trash can incident, then something else.

"Why would she make up such a thing?" Appa asked.

"You hate me," I said in a quiet voice.

Something must have snapped inside Miss Wabash, because her calm tone disappeared, and she turned to my father in a rage. "How should I know what your daughter's motivation is? I can't stand you people. You come to our country, you take jobs from red-blooded Americans, and then you have the gall to complain? You should be grateful, Hagar, to be getting an education in the best country on earth."

Appa jumped up as if he were ready to fight Miss Wabash. "Are you going to let her talk to our daughter like this?"

I opened my mouth to confess. I didn't want my father to get in trouble.

But then the principal intervened. "That's enough, Miss Wabash. Hagar, why don't you step outside." I waited in the hall, thinking about what Miss Wabash had said, that I should be grateful.

My parents emerged. "I'm sorry I didn't believe you," Amma said, hugging me. "They're firing Miss Wabash."

Over the weekend, during the lulls in rain and snow, I took Thatha around the neighborhood for his afternoon walk. One fox lurked by the skeletal rose bushes and one red-breasted robin hopped through a shimmery brown puddle. One deflated balloon hung from a sycamore tree in the neighbor's yard. "But she wouldn't admit it?" my grandfather asked. "If she was willing to admit to some of those things, it seems she would admit to the others." He put on his glasses and peered at me as we shuffled down the street. He waited, breathing heavily, but I said nothing.

There was no pleasure in counting, there was only one of every living thing in the winter snow. Thatha complained that his chest hurt, and went inside, but I stood on the front lawn for a long while. My feet felt cold and moist and tender inside my soggy sneakers. I tried to reignite the old feeling of excitement when I accounted for things. It wouldn't catch.

The next week, there was a substitute teacher in Miss Wabash's place, a gnomish man named Mr. Kaplan who had hair growing in thick tufts from his ears. During the math hour, he assigned the same problems to everyone. He did not use colored chalks. Everybody worked alone and there were no advanced problems, and nothing to keep my interest. Frustrated, I chewed my cuticles and made up fraction problems to keep myself occupied. I remembered what my grandfather had said—that numbers were eternal, trustworthy.

At lunch in the cafeteria, Anne passed my table, and unexpectedly, she paused. "What is that?" She was chewing on the end of her wispy blond braid and staring at the black numerology book.

At first I was too startled to answer her. She hadn't spoken to me in months. Finally I said, "It tells me about people based on their birthdate." I told Anne about her personality number and then her karmic number.

"That's not anything like me," said Anne, wrinkling her nose. "I'm not *peaceful.*" All the kids at the table pressed in close around asking me to calculate their numbers. Flustered, I started to count in Tamil. The kids stared at me with uneasy expressions, and with a start, I realized I was so upset I was speaking in the wrong language, and began counting in English again.

After I gave them each the number from their birthdays—not the right ones—everyone agreed I was wrong, and the chorus of their voices in agreement was like the black whirring of wasps. I closed my eyes and opened them again. The vibration that numbers had always possessed—the special thing that connected me to the invisible sense-making structures of the world—was gone. Instead, the world buzzed with an energy entirely unresponsive to me, and the group, an unknown number of children, stopped talking and stared at me.

"That's so dumb," said a boy who had once thrown me against the wall. "You can't tell the future with a stupid book. Dummy."

"Yeah!"

"Yeah!"

After school, I spotted Miss Wabash with her familiar shock of red hair walking with a cardboard box toward the parking lot. "Miss Wabash!" I called. It wasn't too late. This time, I would tell the truth, this time I would say how sorry I was.

But she didn't respond to my calls. I screamed "Miss Wabash!" again and again as I ran across the frosty field, my backpack bouncing off my spine. I slid on a long patch of ice flowering the lawn, and fell and scraped my knee. I jumped back up and raced past the other kids as they strolled towards the street where the school monitor was directing traffic. By the time I reached the parking lot, Miss Wabash was already ensconced in her Volvo, pulling out of a spot.

"Miss Wabash, I'm sorry," I screamed at the car, and beat the car windows with my fists. "Sorry. I'm sorry!"

Miss Wabash looked past me with bloodshot grey eyes and the car kept rolling backward, until it couldn't any further, and then it lurched forward. I ran after the car in the icy lot. I slid on a patch of ice and steadied myself, and started running again, but Miss Wabash was determined to get away from me. The car picked up speed, as it screeched around a turn. Up ahead, the school monitor was turned the other way, directing kids across the crosswalk.

Meanwhile Anne was galloping through a snowdrift in the lot, her blond braids bouncing. In a moment's miscalculation, she lost her balance and dropped to her hands and knees in the car's path. Miss Wabash swerved. The scream of brakes, metal on metal. A quiet thud as the corner of the bumper hit Anne. She landed on her face on the asphalt. My heart stopped. All around me, I heard screaming and wailing and crying. Horrified, I froze. All I could think was: I had done this. Parents and children were running towards Anne, running and falling on the ice. In all the commotion, there was the sound of a woman screaming, get help, get help.

Bobby Jamison stood on the sidewalk, watching. He caught my eye and narrowed his gaze, before turning back to the gathering mob. Before the crowd in dark overcoats surrounded Anne, I saw a streak of blood, a cardinal feather lost in the grey slush.

***

I trudged home through the slush. Thawing ash-colored snow coursed in streams in the gutters alongside me. The ambulance with its bright red lights hurtled past me, and then the fire truck. The air was warmer than it had been, and carried the smells of wet concrete and fresh yeasty bread. I started to count the snowdrop shoots in a neighbor's yard, but when I got to seven, I stopped and shook my head. Numbers would do nothing. Near my house, I stopped and opened my backpack and took out the numerology book. I threw it in the gutter. It sank for a moment, the thin cheap paper dissolving almost immediately in the murky swirling water. For a moment, I was tempted to retrieve the book, yank it out sopping-wet, and study it, lay bare all the mysteries of this new and vicious life. I would discover the eternal wisdom that the first pages of the book promised, the secret answers that had eluded me thus far, for reasons I didn't yet understand. I followed the stream as it carried the book. In a moment, the stream quickened, and the pages were caught in an eddy, which flung it over the metal grates and down into the dark sewer.

It began to rain. A sudden downpour. From the sidewalk outside I could see my grandfather and my mother through the living room window, fighting in raised voices about something, perhaps his heart pills, perhaps the war, perhaps me. Through the glass came the glow of the fire they'd lit in the hearth, the shower of blue and gold sparks. I hoped to go inside and receive the sole remaining comfort I knew existed in the chaotic, terrifying world we had come into—that my mother would run her gentle fingers through my hair and tell me everything would be all right. But I was afraid there was no coming back from what I'd done, so instead I just stood outside, watching firelight animate their faces, until I was drenched. Black smoke unfurled from the top of the chimney, and died in all that rain and wind. I couldn't have known it yet, I suppose, but there was no comfort coming, not for years.

The Fight of the Century

Marko Fong

When Henry Hemmings needed a transistor radio in March 1971, I insisted that he take mine. We were at the long sink in the bathroom during the break between evening study halls. Henry was trimming his goatee with a safety razor and I was applying a marginally effective acne medication to the left side of my face. Henry was sixteen and I was fourteen. We were both in fourth form at the Nathan School, but Henry was already a starter on the football and basketball teams, which made him the coolest guy in our class. I was the only Asian student in the school, which made me more of an oddity than any kind of cool.

"Ali's going to be the champ again," I said.

"He's never stopped being champ," Henry said as he checked his profile in the mirror. "But now no one's going to be able to deny it." Henry patted his hair with his free hand. His afro looked like a black dandelion.

"No one's quicker than Ali," I said. It was a line that I remembered from Sports Illustrated. Nothing more. Henry responded by doing the Ali shuffle and jabbing his razor hand at his reflection. I found myself waiting for him to say 'I am the greatest' as he danced around the bathroom, but he never did.

"And Ali's too smart for Frazier," Henry said.

I nodded. I'd never actually seen Ali or Frazier fight. I wasn't sure that Henry had either even though he had a big poster of Ali on the wall of his study. It hung between Angela Davis and Malcolm X. No one seriously thought that Henry was militant. There weren't many posters of black women back then and the *Autobiography of Malcolm X* had been one of the selections in third form D English, where Nathan stashed its share of the "talented tenth" sent by A Better Chance. ABC was a program that identified promising students from Harlem, Roxbury, West Chicago, Watts, East Oakland, and Bedford Stuyvesant for elite private schools.

"Did you really ask Corcoran if you could go to Lowell to watch the fight on closed circuit?" I said as I emptied my red plastic water basin into the black trough sink.

"Yeah, but he said, not on a school night."

"Figures."

There was no way the Cork would have said "yes." I knew that Henry knew that too. I admired him for asking anyway.

"I told him that this is Ali. This is history. But he said it's just a boxing match. It's not Andre Watts or Gordon Parks."

Gordon Parks had visited the school a year ago and spent two days with Nathan's twelve black students talking about photography and his book *The Learning Tree*. Otherwise, I'm not sure that our headmaster would have known the name. I wouldn't have either.

Henry lightly tapped the razor against the sink. "You know, it would almost be worth it to go to Lowell anyway."

"How would you get there?"

"Hitch."

No one was really going to pick up a black teenager outside the gates of the Nathan School after dark. The closest black families lived in Fitchburg and the town folk knew better than to mess with the school by helping students slip away. It also struck me that Henry Hemmings probably wouldn't get in much trouble for trying it. No prep school was going to kick out its best athlete, especially if he happened to be an

African American scholarship student on the honor roll. The publicity would hurt fundraising.

"How would you get back?"

"Maybe I wouldn't come back."

I stared at Henry waiting for him to smile, but he didn't. I put my wash basin back on its hook above the sink where it hung in a row with the twenty-five other basins for the boys in our dorm.

I hated being at the school, but I wouldn't have hated the school if I were as popular as Henry. It had never occurred to me that he'd even consider going home to Baltimore. In two years, he was virtually guaranteed a full scholarship to Harvard or Yale. After that, who knew? This was the whole idea behind A Better Chance.

"You know the fight's probably on the radio," I said. "It's not as good as closed circuit, but it's also not thirty dollars."

Henry put down his razor.

"I have a transistor radio… In case you don't get a ride to the movie theater in Lowell."

"Don't you want to listen to the fight yourself?"

"I have two, it's no big deal."

This was only partly true. I had two transistor radios, one that worked and one that didn't. The bell rang and signaled the fact that we had three minutes to return to our studies. But the fight was all any of us talked about for days on end. One of the sixth formers had set up a betting line with Frazier, the mild favorite. Even some of the masters were talking about it, though most insisted that they'd never bet on a prize fight.

It split the school. It seemed that everyone I wanted to like was rooting for Ali. If some boy were for Ali, I liked him better. Henry Hemmings was Ali's biggest fan at Nathan and everyone knew it. It surprised me that more of our classmates weren't following the lead of the most popular kid in the form. Instead, most of the white kids were lining up for Frazier. For the two weeks before the fight, Brad Bronson would start talking loudly at breakfast about Frazier's power and the fact that Ali had never been much of a puncher. Somehow, the chatter always got punctuated with "Frazier's going to put Ali in his place." I stared at the freckles that dotted Brad's face and shook my head. All I knew was that I rooted for Ali because he said "No."

When Henry knocked on my study door just before the end of second study hall, I was pleasantly surprised.

"Lucky, do you have that transistor radio?"

I pulled my working radio from my desk drawer, checked to make sure the battery hadn't died, and offered him the single white earphone that went with it. Henry looked at me.

"What do I need this for?"

"You don't want to get caught."

One of the oddities of Nathan School was that we didn't sleep in rooms. During the evening we had studies, usually shared with another boy, but at night we slept in a long hall that was a cross between a barracks and a horse stall. A thin wooden wall that reached halfway to the twelve foot ceiling divided each bed. The front of each "cubicle" was marked by a turquoise curtain on a wooden dowel. When he founded the school in 1881, Josiah Saltonstall had determined that a community based on trust could not have anything resembling physical privacy. The school had no locked doors, no bathroom stall fronts, or shower curtains. The result was a cross between a modern version of Sparta and some gay boarding school fantasy.

Henry looked at the earphone suspiciously then handed it back to me. "I'll just hold it next to the pillow."

Three minutes later, there was a second knock at my door. Garrison Cottrell was from a small town in North Carolina, and he was the least popular kid in the class. He had the broad chest and muscular arms of an adult male, the product of summers lifting and carrying things with grown men, but Cottrell was too clumsy to be an athlete. Cottrell had been inspired by a teacher to study the dictionary and read the encyclopedia and that had brought him to the attention of Nathan.

"Lucky, this may not be expeditious, but I was contemplating whether I might be able to promissory a transistor radio from your person."

"Why are you asking me, Cottrell?"

"Henry Hemmings communicated to me that he got one from you. It's exigent that I be able to sequester one this evening, Lucky Tang. Besides, you're of oriental extraction and that is the locality from which these electronic devices originate."

"But Henry has my transistor radio."

"He elocuted to me that you have a brace of these auditory transducers."

"But I might want to listen to the fight too."

"You lent one to Hemmings. This isn't equitable. Is it because I'm a Negro?"

It was no mystery why Cottrell wasn't liked. In a year and a half at Nathan, he'd never shown a sign of being able to take hints. Two weeks into third form year he acquired the secret nickname *Matrell.* The MA was for "malaprop," but Cottrell persisted even after finding out. In the dining hall at breakfast, he often wound up sitting alone. Even the other black students, who had their own table in the back corner, tired of him. They said he was 'too obviously country.' Cottrell hadn't known when to shower, change underwear, or when not to stare at the younger faculty wives. But his popularity may have improved slightly in the last two weeks before the fight as a result of the impressions he started doing of Joe Frazier. As far as I was concerned, Cottrell was in the wrong camp.

"You're rooting for Frazier, Cottrell. I'm not going to help you do that."

Cottrell's build resembled Frazier's and he could do the face. He'd even found a hat like the one Frazier wore from time to time, and guys would say "Hey, Smokin' Joe you gonna beat Ali?" and Cottrell would smile. But now he shook his head at me as if I'd betrayed him.

My own strategy at Nathan hadn't been much different from Cottrell's. I spent my first three months pretending to read really fast and playing chess blindfolded. The latter was something I could do. It was just that I couldn't play all that well with or without looking at the board. I just tended to be too careless. Neither of us had a way to fit in at Nathan, but I'd at least figured out how to get by.

"Sorry, Cottrell. I'm sure someone else will have a radio you can borrow." He looked defeated.

On the big day, Cottrell was at the end of the corridor in blue boxer shorts pretending that his cubicle curtain was Ali. He had his Smokin' Joe hat on, and was jabbing at the turquoise cloth on the wooden dowel. We tried to ignore him because we were on a mission. A few of us took a shot at getting our dorm master Mr. Hall to let us stay up to listen to the fight. I was sandwiched in between Bradley and my study mate, Tom Perkins. Henry was nearby. We knew that Mr. Hall wasn't going to allow it, but we had to try. "Guys, I don't want to get in trouble myself. I'd love to hear it too."

"But we want to know who you're rooting for," Brad said.

Mr. Hall was also the hockey coach, so we knew he had a certain respect for fights, though in the private school league it was more like throwing your gloves to the ice followed by a push or two.

Our dorm master shrugged. "I think what Ali did was braver than anything anyone could do in the ring."

Brad looked at him with a blank expression. "You're rooting for Ali?"

"I didn't say that, Bradley. I said that I admired what he did."

"Mr. Hall, what do you think about Frazier calling Ali, Clay?"

Perkins said. "Don't you think that Ali is making too big a deal about it?"

Perkins had come from one of those Manhattan private schools that seemed to be Nathan School South. The dozen or so boys in the form from those places were all familiar with Nathan's various written and unwritten rules. They understood that getting in a little bit of trouble was actually a good thing because it showed "spirit," and they demonstrated "poise" by knowing just when to be honest about how hard they'd tried or wanted something. Midway through the year, I was sorry to have asked Perkins to share a study with me because it was increasingly clear that our association was Perkins's attempt to prove that he wasn't just another member of the Buckley, Dalton, and St. Bernard's tribe. They had once owned Nathan School and all that came after it, but now had to give the appearance of sharing.

Mr. Hall shrugged. "Guys, I don't hate Joe Frazier. They're both great fighters. It's just a boxing match, even if they are calling it the fight of the century."

Henry stepped in closer. "It's more than a boxing match, Mr. Hall. Ali is the greatest. We're not going to see anything like this again."

"I'm sorry, Henry. I'd really like to let you guys hang out and listen, but you know it's going to get too rowdy and then Mr. Corcoran will be down here. Look, I know some of you have transistor radios. After lights out, I'm not going to be checking beds."

The actual fight started at 10:15, ten minutes after lights. Muhammad Ali had fought just twice after a two year absence from the ring. In his absence, Joe Frazier had not just beaten every other boxer in the world; he had knocked all but three of them out. The only consolation for Ali fans was that the former champ had an easier time beating Oscar Bonavena a few months ago than Frazier had. I lay on my bed trying to picture Madison Square Garden. I saw it in black and white and full of cigar smoke because that's the way it looked on TV.

"Frazier takes round one," someone from a few cubicles up announced. "They're saying that Ali looks rusty."

My stomach tightened. Brad began to chant, "Frazier, Frazier." I started to feel sick.

Cottrell joined in and then there were about half a dozen other voices chanting Frazier's name until one of the prefects jumped into the mix.

"Are you guys idiots? he said. The sixth formers, as the oldest boys in the school, were dispersed across the lower form dorms to serve as steadying influences. "I don't care if you listen, but don't be stupid."

"Frazier just knocked down Ali."

Ali was two years older than Frazier. He had also spent two years idle. My heart dropped into my stomach and a gasp ran across the cubicles.

"Suckers!" It was my studymate, Perkins.

"You asshole, Perkins." Someone shouted what I'd wanted to say for some time.

Then I heard Henry's voice. When Henry spoke, the other boys didn't interrupt, even in the dark. "Guys, Ali took the first three rounds. They said Frazier's head snapped back twice. Please, shut up so we can hear the fight." But Bradley broke the silence a few minutes later. "They're saying that Ali's trying to out-slug Frazier. He's not dancing and Ali's looking tired."

For the past three weeks, Joe Louis had been saying that world class fighters had to fight to stay in condition. He was like a broken record and fans rooting for Frazier fell in step. Henry dismissed them all one day. On the way from morning chapel service, he broke it down. *"Joe*

Louis is colored. Joe Frazier is a Negro. Ali is black. Given the choice, I'm rooting for black."

"Frazier's got him in the corner," Bradley announced.

A chant of "Frazier, Frazier" started again. "Put Ali in his place," someone yelled.

"I'm trying to listen to the fight," Henry said. "I don't want the prefects to come back and take away our radios." Henry was calm, but firm.

"You mean put Clay in his place."

It was Perkins. Because it was Perkins, it might have stopped, but Bradley and Cottrell began chanting it in rhythm.

I sat up on the side of my bed shaking. I was confounded by their chants. Most of my classmates were wealthy white kids. What did they care about Joe Frazier? Was it really about Frazier-Ali at all? Most of them didn't even follow boxing.

For several rounds, nothing exciting happened except when Perkins and Bradley tried more "fake" updates by announcing first that Ali had been knocked down, and then that he'd run out of the ring. Around what should have been the 9th or 10th round, I noticed that no one was bothering to correct them. I pretended to go to the bathroom. I figured that I could head there, check to see if anyone was in the hall, and then slip into my study to listen to the fight there on my clock radio. My aunt had given it to me a year ago as a "going away" gift. She didn't know that our cubicles didn't have electrical outlets and that a very loud bell rang every morning at 6:45.

As I slipped into the hallway that connected the cubicles, I noticed that the curtain fronting Cottrell's cubicle was fluttering and making a "Whuffing" noise. Cottrell was punching the inside making like Joe Frazier. The boys next to Cottrell's cubicle were urging him on, *Faster Joe, faster, hit him harder.*

The light in the bathroom was already on. I took a few steps in and found Henry sitting on the toilet with my transistor radio pressed against his Afro.

"Too crazy in there," I whispered.

"Same here."

"What's been happening in the fight?"

Henry shook his head and looked down at the white tile floor.

"Ali's wearing down. Frazier keeps getting him in the corner and hitting him in the body. They're fighting Frazier's fight."

"And that's not good."

Henry nodded.

"Frazier's smarter than I thought. He took the punishment early knowing that Ali might wear himself out trying for the KO."

I nodded back, but Henry cocked his head and stared at me.

"Where's your second radio?"

"I was just going to listen on the clock radio in my study."

"But you haven't been listening have you? When Bradley and Perkins were lying about the first rounds, you would have been the first one to correct them. You didn't."

My stomach churned at having been caught in a lie. I didn't really care as much about Ali and the fight. I had just wanted to be Henry's friend.

"I thought if you could listen on the radio, you might not hitch to Lowell and maybe get in trouble."

Henry made a black power fist with his free hand. "I wasn't really going to go, but now I sort of wish I had."

"They're idiots. Bradley, Perkins, all of them."

"And Cottrell. He doesn't even know that they're laughing at him."

I'd been afraid to add Cottrell's name to the list in Henry's presence.

"So, Lucky Tang, you lent me your only radio."

Henry held it in his palm and studied it. I shrugged. He turned the volume dial with his thumb and motioned for me to take a seat on the toilet next to him as we listened to the Fight of the Century dwindle away with Ali getting knocked down, but not out, in the 15th round.

We didn't wait for the judges' decision and Henry insisted that I go back to the dorm first. Before I did, he offered his hand for a soul handshake. Then he handed me back my radio.

"Don't you want to hear the decision?"

Henry shook his head, "I'd rather not."

I slipped back into my cubicle and heard Henry follow a couple of minutes later. I slipped in my white earphone and was the one to announce, "Unanimous decision for Frazier."

A muffled cheer went up. Actually, Ali had accomplished a rather amazing thing. He'd spent two years away from fighting and almost beat a younger man in prime shape who had knocked out almost all of his opponents. I just wasn't old enough to understand the notion of valor in defeat.

Everyone was still talking about the fight the next morning. In Mr. Woolery's Latin class, the name Cassius Marcellus came up in Cicero and the class roared with laughter when Perkins was called to recite and slipped in "qui Frazier occidere."

It wasn't quite correct, but the meaning was clear enough, Cassius who was knocked down and killed by Frazier. Even Mr. Woolery, perhaps the sternest of the classics teachers, smiled and let the class indulge in chants of "Frazier Cassius occidet."

Mr. Woolery may have been trying to make up for September of third form when he had inadvertently exposed Cottrell four days into his Nathan career. Woolery had asked the class when Caesar had been assassinated and, after a couple boys missed, Cottrell had raised a hand to guess "1600, Sir."

"1600, Mr. Cottrell?" It was Woolery's way of hinting that he wanted you to change your answer quickly.

"Yes sir, 1600 A.D.?"

Woolery's eyes widened, he slapped the side of his face, and exclaimed, "Why the man's crazy!"

For three days, that story was stirred up with reports about Cottrell's poor hygiene. And eighteen months later, Cottrell was chanting "Frazier Cassius occident" along with the other boys.

By lunch the phrase was all across the fourth form. Cottrell and several of the Manhattan tribe sat at a table chanting it every few minutes. Henry was at the black students table in the corner. They all pretended not to notice the chanting.

I didn't talk to Henry for most of the day. We didn't have any classes together even though the fourth form had just 44 boys. I could sit at the black table from time to time, but understood that it wasn't a regular thing. When the custom started the school had been horrified, but the black students had insisted. They wanted time to be black. Mr. Corcoran had tried to compromise by moving them to a middle table, but the black students insisted on one in the far corner where they sat in their coats and ties, laughing and grooming their Afros with metal picks.

I noticed that most students, including Bradley, were coming up to Henry individually to tell him that they were sorry that Ali lost. Henry would shrug. "He's still the champ," he said, but he said it softly.

I assumed that the "Fight of the Century" would slip into Nathan history, but it didn't. Cottrell wouldn't allow it. One day he stood in the middle of the mat after varsity basketball practice, making like Joe Frazier. He was wearing a pair of fat boxing gloves and a leather headset. I was putting the balls and the first aid kit away in the storage closet of the weight room. Apparently, Mr. Wicks, the school's 68 year old PE teacher, had let him try them on under the guise of teaching Cottrell some boxing basics. He was showing Cottrell how to take the loop out of his jab to make his left fist snap instead of slap. Mr. Wicks had fought Golden Gloves as a boy growing up on the Southside of Boston. He was the only Nathan faculty member without an Ivy League degree, and the only one whose accent matched the kitchen staff's.

I stopped to listen to Mr. Wicks tell Cottrell about the "real fight of the century," between Jack Johnson and Jim Jeffries. Wicks told Cottrell that he once met Jim Jeffries. "A hero in Southie after the war. But he wasn't a nice man, Cottrell. I'm glad Johnson won. Before there was Joe Louis, there was Jack Johnson and Johnson was special."

Masters and students at the school were nice to Cottrell most of the time, or they were at least polite, until they discovered that they could no longer deal with Cottrell's inability to understand prep school manners, like the fact that there were dozens of ways to say "no" without actually saying "no," or that "let's get together" was a way to end a conversation and not a serious invitation unless there was an actual time and place attached to it. This was one of the few times I'd seen someone actually be kind to Cottrell.

"Did you ever meet Jack Johnson, Mr. Wicks?"

"I would have liked to."

"You must have been a very good boxer when you were young."

"I held my own Cottrell. But you're a very strong young man and a tough one. You could hold your own too."

Cottrell's eyes widened and he nodded his head.

"I need to go home to have dinner with Mrs. Wicks; can you put the gloves away in my office when you're done?"

"Thanks, Mr. Wicks."

Cottrell snapped off a series of jabs towards the mirror as I pretended to stay busy in the storage closet. Bradley and Perkins were fresh from playing squash and they cheered him on.

"Hey, it's Joe Frazier, undisputed heavyweight champion of the world."

Cottrell showed off his hook followed by a series of textbook jabs. He actually appeared to have a knack for boxing.

"Where'd you get the gloves, Cottrell?"

"They're Mr. Wicks.'"

"Does he know you have them?"

"Yes, of course. He was showing me how to box."

"I asked him to show me and he told me he didn't do that anymore," Perkins said.

"Are you saying that I'm a prevaricator?"

There was a shift in Cottrell's voice as it went from slow and vaguely southern to his more usual way of talking.

"No, of course not."

Perkins began to dance on the wrestling mat. He was tall and skinny, and wore his hair in a long brown ponytail.. He held his fists up with the thumb tucked under his fingers.

"So, show me what you've learned Joe Frazier!"

"Come on, Perkins, cut it out," Bradley said.

We didn't hear Henry come in. He stood at the edge of the wrestling mat. "Guys, what's going on here?" he said.

Perkins danced around mugging with his face. "Cottrell was going to show me how to fight," he said. Then he started singing, "Float like a butterfly sting like a bee."

I was on the edge of the wrestling mat. A crowd of boys began to gather round.

"Don't do this Cottrell!" Henry said softly.

Cottrell was standing with his gloves in defensive position.

"Henry, you be Ali. You can do Ali better than Perkins," someone shouted.

Henry shook his head and held his hand out to signify that he wanted nothing to do with it.

"Henry, Henry, put Frazier in his place."

Henry turned his back to the wrestling mat. Perkins kept dancing around Cottrell, tapping at his boxing gloves and slapping him playfully on his headgear.

"Come on Cottrell. Show us Smokin' Joe!"

Cottrell was trembling, but his eyes were intense and clear. He put the full force of his body behind his right hand and hit Perkins straight on the nose. Perkins went down immediately, screaming.

"What the fuck? We were just playing. I was kidding around. Don't you get anything?"

But something had let loose in Cottrell. He dove to the floor and continued hitting Perkins. Perkins started to squeal, "Get him off of me!"

As his studymate, I probably should have been the one who walked Perkins and his broken nose back to the infirmary, but I didn't.

It took a few days to sort out and I had to meet with Mr. Corcoran three times to explain what I saw. It was decided that Mr. Wicks would retire at the end of the spring, and Perkins was sent back to East 70th and Park Avenue for two days for starting the fight. Three days later Mr. Corcoran called our form into his parlor after dinner. We knew it was about Garrison Cottrell, the only boy from Rocky Mount, North Carolina to ever go to the Nathan School.

We sat in a circle as we waited for Mr. Corcoran, a kindly man who wore big horned-rimmed glasses that made his large eyes look even wider. When he wasn't called the "Cork," we called him the "Bull Frog." He started slowly.

"I'm very sorry to tell you that Garrison has gone home to North Carolina and he won't be returning to Nathan. I want to make it clear that we've mutually decided that it isn't in his best interests to return to the school."

Perkins sat on the other side of the parlor from me; he nodded solemnly at the news from behind a clear plastic mask that suited him in some weird way. There was a rumor that Perkins' father, a New York attorney, had threatened to go to the Boston Globe, something that Manhattan attorneys did instead of threatening to sue.

"Garrison tried very hard to make it work at Nathan. I've spoken to the masters and we are confident that the school tried its best to help Garrison adjust, but it has become clear that this would be more difficult than any of us anticipated. We have also spoken with the scholarship group A Better Chance, and they have agreed as well that this is best for Garrison…"

Corcoran turned towards Henry. "I've met with the other Negro students at the school and they have agreed that it would be difficult for Garrison to succeed at Nathan at this point. We have told Garrison's grandmother that the school will do whatever it can to help Garrison in the future, and that includes helping him to find a college. I'd now like to give you some time for questions."

Henry looked away.

After an awkward moment, hands shot up.

"Mr. Corcoran, was Garrison expelled?"

"It was a mutual agreement."

"If he hadn't agreed, would he have been expelled?"

"I can't answer that Bradley. If he had only hit Tom the one time, he would have only been suspended. We were very concerned that he aggravated the fight. Tom had to spend two days in the hospital."

I raised my hand.

"But Mr. Corcoran, Cottrell didn't start it."

"Lucky, we're well aware of that, but it's also clear that Tom was only joking. The rector built the school around trust. Garrison's actions violated that trust."

I looked away from Perkins. There were dozens of questions after that about Cottrell, Mr. Wicks, and some need to supervise boys in boxing gloves. Then there was the last question of the evening.

"Is there some way we can write to Cottrell?"

"Yes, that would be nice. You can give me the letter if you like. I'm going down there personally to visit, or Mrs. Gage can provide you with his address tomorrow morning."

None of us ever took the time to write to Garrison.

A week later, I moved into Cottrell's single study, claiming that I wanted the privacy to study more. Bradley moved in with Perkins. From that point on, I stayed apart in my way from their tribe.

It was a quiet spring after that. The only excitement was when one of the crew team's fours actually won interschools and got a chance to race at Henley on Thames in the summer. The boys in our class continued to laugh at Henry's jokes and they sat near him in the dining hall on those occasions when he didn't sit at the black table. Just before prize day in June, a rumor circulated that Cottrell had walked into a girl's house, stripped off his clothes at her front door, and asked her to marry him. The phrase "electro-shock" turned up in some versions of the story.

Some members of the class found the story funny, but I noticed that Henry refused to talk about the rumor. When I saw him in the library a few days later, I tried to tell him the news of Ali's next fight. Then somehow I found myself talking about Cottrell.

"I could have been Cottrell," I said, "just without the naked thing."

Henry shrugged, "If I didn't play football, I might have been too."

"You, no way," I said.

"It doesn't feel right. The bigger idiot stays and Cottrell gets sent home. Who knows what that's like?"

Henry shrugged. "Told Corcoran that I didn't think Cottrell could make it here after the fight, but I never said that it was right for him not to keep trying. No one asked us that."

At prize day, Henry Hemmings was honored as the most outstanding fourth former and the most athletic boy in the "middle forms." The entire form applauded the announcements.

When Henry didn't return in the fall, I was one of the few who wasn't shocked. According to another black scholarship student from Baltimore, Henry was saying that he missed his girlfriend too much. 'He was really homesick, he just never let on.'

Even for sixteen year olds, it was hard to understand why someone would choose a girlfriend over a full scholarship to Harvard. Others said that Henry had broken his wrist over the summer and wasn't going to get to play football or basketball during our 5th form year. Henry got calls and letters from us begging him to come back. He never wrote. The school lobbied hard as well. Mr. Corcoran apparently visited twice over the summer and even brought Bobby Watkins, a recent Nathan graduate who was playing football at Penn to coax Henry back. There was even a story that Henry's girlfriend was offered a scholarship at Concord Academy, a nearby girl's school that had recently gone coed. It didn't seem to matter that Henry's girlfriend wasn't much of a student.

I never wrote or phoned Henry. I did sign a card from the entire form inviting him to our graduation. I understood that he was done with Nathan. We had long since stopped talking about the Fight of the Century, especially now that Frazier had been knocked down six times in two rounds by George Foreman. When Ali beat Frazier in the second fight, I was tempted to send a postcard to Henry Hemmings, but was afraid that he wouldn't care to hear from me.

When it came time to choose a college, another black student from Baltimore reported that he'd heard through the ABC grapevine that Henry was going to the Hampton Institute, an all black school in Virginia. He sighed, "He could have gone anywhere even after going back to Baltimore, and he could have still gone to Harvard."

I failed to get into Harvard or Yale. My parents never said it, but they acted disappointed and embarrassed about my going to Duke which in most normal places would have been an opportunity to brag about. Nathan's college advisor told my parents, "Lucky just never seemed to take to this environment the way he might have. He does what he's supposed to do, but he's never blossomed." I graduated, but refused to fit in after both Cottrell and Henry left and I took Cottrell's old study.

Perkins went to Yale and Bradley to Columbia. No one ever found Garrison Cottrell again. Years later, I was driving though his town and was shocked to find that everyone in the town was black and the only two businesses were a gas station and a grocery store. There were no Cottrells in the phone book.

When Ali won the title from George Foreman by stealing Frazier's strategy from the fight of the century, I tried to imagine Henry Hemmings jabbing and dancing with his razor blade in hand.

Thirty five years later, I was shocked to hear from him on Facebook. He was a doctor in North Carolina. I had returned to California and married a woman who had attended only public schools and never known that anything else was possible. We never talked about my high school experience in New England.

I was at home surfing the net when I got a chat request from Henry Hemmings.

"I remember, you had books of baseball statistics and played chess with yourself. I was totally blown away by that."

I typed back, "It's so embarrassing, I was such a nerd."

"No, you were just gifted. And I remember that you lent me your only radio."

I started to cry.

"What's the matter?" my wife asked.

"I'm just chatting with an old friend from high school."

My wife blinked. "I thought you didn't have any friends from Nathan."

"But there was Henry Hemmings," I said. "He was the smartest guy in the entire school. And he's doing just fine."

The Woman and the Branch

Rachel Eliza Griffiths

I knew. I knew. My mother gave me
her bluebird of happiness. Carrying the glass
inside my skin to school, I was young.
Show us what you have, the world said.
I was polishing somebody's rapture.
It wasn't mine. Not my paradise
or my mother's love, but oh god
how it shone. I could never tell
which bird was singing. I went home
like a canticle to its branch. I flew
through gray leaves away from
childhood. I gave my mother answers I knew,
didn't ask whether there was another color –
was blue right after all? Was happiness
a song to be shattered?
I couldn't explain the frailty, how
the figurine had cracked
when I looked through its life.

i watch papa bury our dog in a grave the size of a pond

Raven Jackson

mauve, sprigs of oleander—
ceilings shedding water

stains in shapes of crooked
eyes—my jaws lock in mid-sentence

and hands cover your last white
leg with dirt
                                        i name it

a lighthouse: a jar full of salt:
a longitude line   undone

summer barely opening her dress
but the shutters singing

Lock Butter

Hope Johnson

I be a tender root
a mere indecisive tangle
that has been smashed
and twisted
and rolled smooth
between her caramel palms

woven and shaped into stories
passed down from granny
to momma to grand-baby
that grew and curled
latched and knotted
into strong and wise
black and woman and poem

I carry the scent
of an old lemon picker's hands
of a little girl's bare legs
running through summer weeds

the golden strand
that coils leans toward her lips

when she speaks   writes
hugged in scents of chalkboard
cedar pencils   blank pages

I be immersed
in the butter of her name
thicklike mud still wet
on God's fingertips

the drop
that became an ocean
tumbling down her waist
the texture of orange peels
and wild Kentucky twangs

What Lies Beneath

Cynthia Manick

Today I am elbow deep
in some animal's belly

pulling out the heart and stomach
for my mother's table

brown rubber soles blood slicked
the swing of twin blades

cuts a whole village worth of pelts,
coon, carved bones for ladies

jewelry and coats. These hands
can ground down rock and gold

call a man *sweet dusty*, mold
knots of spit and hair like clay

until a baby's head is perfectly round.
These hands are good for killing—

I feel this knowing rise

like different names for fire.

Every bone has a ghost–
the smallest, a stirrup in the ear

whispers walk carefully there
you come from a dark tribe.

Still Life

Cecca Austin Ochoa

I lie and say this scar's a gift from my cat. Three inches long, hypertrophic, silver and purple; it's like the hidden seam in taxidermy, only inside out. People look doubtful—including Ana, who's got more scars than a lightning tree—but when they meet my cat, wild thing, they believe. She's feral with six toes, a clipped left ear and a face like a chupacabra. I put food out for her on the windowsill when I hear her purring, then see those glowing lantern eyes in the night. She doesn't like to be touched. Only when she steps through the window onto the kitchen table and pushes her fanged face into my hand, do I run my fingers through her matted tabby coat. I click my tongue for her, my wild thing. She disappears for months at a time then suddenly shows up. She's like Ana in that way.

Ana was wild with excitement when she called me out of the blue, this after a year of giving me a cold shoulder. She told me she was engaged to Jake. Truth told, I'd been waiting for her to dump that fool. You see, Ana's my girl, somos guanaca-americanas. First generation Salvadoreñas born in the empire. I've known Ana since I was twelve years old. We met in the 90's in San Francisco, at a free summer day-camp—provided by the city to keep kids like us from spending our whole vacation on the couch in front of a TV. In my case, a plastic chair in a hospital lounge, waiting for Ma to finish her chemo treatments. At camp, a smiling woman with a long blonde braid taught us how to draw dogs with #2 pencils: two ovals, a circle for the head, triangles for ears, a trapezoid nose, add the legs and a tail. I colored my dog pink and silver, Ana's had blood dripping from its mouth; we looked at each other and saw artists. By fall, we moved through the world like conjoined twins: Raquel and Ana, a four-armed two-headed beast tumbling down the halls of our Junior High School. We dressed in black, wore purple lipstick, got sugar high on gas station Icees and scribbled *live wild and die free* on bus station shelters. I knew Ana like I knew myself.

Problem was, I knew Jake, too. Met him a few years ago, when he answered my ad: caramel skinned seductress, girlfriend experience. I waited for him on 43rd in my high-tops and cotton dress, surprised by his dopey smile. The springy way he walked in his leather oxfords as we passed the 90 cents a minute jack-off booths and the I <3 New York T-shirt shops, up to Martina's apartment. The apartment had a king-sized bed in the living room, a side table with vanilla scented candles and a glass vase filled with marbles, for the occasional rose. The deadbolt-locked bedroom door, where Martina lived, hid behind a velvet curtain. Jake wanted me to spoon him, he wanted to brush my long black hair, he wanted to practice his Spanish pointing to different parts of my body with a crooked index finger. "Comeré el dedo," I said and bared my teeth. Then, he slapped me.

Flipping burgers. That's most of the guys I see. You want cheese on that? No one had slapped me before. Ears still ringing, I pulled my scalpel from under the pillow and growled, *leave now*. "Guess you don't like it rough," he said and put his hands up with a smirk. But I saw fear flash in his eyes; didn't take him long to get dressed. What would he know about what I like? I'm not in the business to make friends or get disrespected; I'm in it to pay the bills, and I won't see just anyone. There are women who will. One girl saw all the blacklisted clients. She took pride in it, like she was tougher than the rest of us. She wore scarves to cover up the bruises around her neck, but she'd vanished. No one could find her and not because we hadn't looked.

That's how it is: People come and they go. Who knows where. I came to New York to work on my art, and 'cause Ana's here. Eventually, I'll live in the desert with solar panels and a house made from mud. Belong to no government, spend no money, make no profit for myself or anyone else. Una mujer salvaje. When I disappear, you'll never find me.

Not long after she'd broken up with Mauricio, Ana brought that baboso, Jake, to my group show in Chelsea. My piece Deer/man came from an ongoing series about the legacy of war, something we Salvadoreñas know a thing about. Ana's mother left El Salvador after her daughter, Ana's sister, was murdered and her husband disappeared by los escuadrónes de la muerte. The death squads. Wiped off the face of the knowable earth. Deer/man had the head of a stag attached to a silicon torso of a man. The deer skin tapered into a V at the solar plexus. The hunted and the hunter stitched together. Deer/man protruded from a mirrored wall-mount shaped like a crest. I wanted people to see their expressions as they thought, poor deer.

While explaining my work in rogue taxidermy to another artist — how I take my scalpel and shave away bits of fat and sticky veins before rubbing salt into the hide; how I carefully diagram muscle structure before making a plaster cast— I saw Ana from across the gallery, and waved her over. Ana's beautiful: Full-lipped, gallon-sized breasts, wide hips, narrow but soft waist: A two-hourglass figure. She popped out of the crowd by my side, then Jake by hers.

When I saw him, my cheek burned and my mouth went dry, as though someone had stuffed a stocking down my throat. She introduced me and I smiled helplessly, thinking, of all the eight million people in New York, how the fuck did this creep sniff out my girl? Not to mention, I'd never told Ana how I butter my bread. She whispered in my ear, "He's the one," but I could barely hear over the sound of my heartbeat. I excused myself and turned back to the artist, loudly continuing to tell her how I dismember the cadavers, the difficulty of removing the cheeks. She patted my shoulder and headed to the bar.

"No, no," Ana was saying to Jake, as I turned back to them. "Raquel's sculptures are about embodiment. About historical memory."

"It's animal abuse," Jake said pushing his sorry hands into the pockets of his prep-school khaki's. He ignored me and stared at Ana with an expression like he'd hung a vacancy sign in the blue windows of his eyes.

I explained that factory farming was animal abuse. That I only used roadkill. For conceptual and ethical reasons.

"Ethical?" he asked. "So, do you make enough money to support yourself with your art?"

My face flushed and I grabbed Ana's hand. "¿Como lo conociste?"

"The internets."

"He reminds me of Mauricio," I said. Ana dropped my hand and shot me a wounded look—those doll-eyes wide, lips parted like I'd stuck her with a knife. Two years later when I ran into her, after she'd married Jake, I'd remember that look. Betrayal. But, by then, she knew what she'd been stuck with.

If I'd been thinking clearly, I would have pulled the gag out that night in the Chelsea. I'd never told Ana about my work 'cause every time I thought about coming clean, I'd remember all the afternoons we spent side by side on the pink carpet of my Ma's living room floor pretending to do homework, but actually plotting our art world establishment takeover. She went on to work for an arts non- profit for the children of immigrants. I wanted her to think of me as the artist, not the puta. But I wasn't thinking clearly.

I called her up a few days later to apologize, knowing she'd be pissed I'd brought up Mauricio. Ana had been with him for years. When I moved to New York in 2005, I took the train over to South Slope, where they lived together. I'd found their building and walked up the four flights of stairs, expecting to be warmed by the face of an old friend. Together again! But, Ana stood at the door cold and thin, too thin, and pale. Only her eyes gave heat, but not the warming kind. I didn't see Mauricio that day, but I saw his bruises on Ana's arms. Deep purple thumb prints on her bicep. I'd run my fingers across the ragged cuts that scarred her wrist. "I didn't do it to hurt myself," she said. "I did it to hurt him."

I tried to warn Ana, "That guy Jake es malo. I can see it in his eyes."

"No, girl," Ana said. "You're not seeing what I'm seeing."

Jake sent an email to my work account asking for my "professional discretion in the matter." He promised they really were in love. That she needed his help. I couldn't imagine what she needed him for, so I didn't reply. I tried calling Ana a few more times, suggested hang outs, but she was always too busy. Even though I worried about her, I kept my distance. I wanted her to be Ana, to stand on her own two feet, not wrapped around somebody else's.

A few weeks after running into Jake, I saw another ex-client out in the world. Michael. After working at Martina's, I sometimes went for dinner at an Italian restaurant in the Theater District. A place I couldn't actually afford, but justified as self-care. I looked up from my food to see him with a woman his age and two teenage kids, sitting right across the restaurant from me. I'd seen Michael every week for two years before he disappeared. He'd told me he was single. He'd said something about moving to Westchester to be near his dying mother. I can't remember.

What I did remember, while watching him delicately slice his steak, was the hotel on Lexington. A cold light beamed through a floor to ceiling window. I laid my hand on his warm chest and watched his breath quicken and tears stream out of his eyes. "I didn't know I could feel this way again," he said.

"I'm so glad you can feel," I replied and let my eyes beam with joy. Not for his emotions, but 'cause I knew each tear would turn to money in my hand. Michael and his family all looked unhappy, like no one could bother to think of anything to say. The woman, especially. She stared at the single noodle skewered on her fork, apparently lacking all appetite.

The teenage girl knocked over her water glass, and the woman chucked a napkin at her. Michael looked up with a face full of desperation. He saw me: The secret. He met my eyes, but looked right through.

I felt my body slide out of focus. Could anyone actually see me? Was I disappearing from the knowable earth? I decided then, the next time Ana came around I'd tell her everything. But almost a year went by until she called, and a lot happened that year.

I had two shows, and started with a new instructor who would say things like *taxidermy is a still life that used to have a heartbeat.* I'd look at the piles of fur and tooth and glass eyes. I'd think about Ana, our after school adventures, that moment she turned into the sun, squinted her eyes and sent me a purple lipstick air kiss through the wind. I'd imagine Ma, still a girl, in the bed of a pick up truck tracing the constellations with her eyes. She rode North—to the very country funding the violence she'd escaped from—carrying with her a civil war in her own body; the sleeping cancer cells awoke and grew wild.

I called Ma, who I'd barely spoken to since leaving California five years earlier. When I left, she had remission status, three triumphant daughters, one tit, a mountain of medical bills, and a lab technician's cell phone number. That number was the only thing on her mind. She didn't sound happy to hear from me. "Vos sabéis que your sisters are driving me crazy," she said and made a sound like a whimper. "You're the only one of all the girls who can make it on her own."

"You ok?"

"Come back. Aqui te esperamos."

"Mamá, no. I'm moving to the desert."

"Don't let your ideas get in the way of our life. Besides, how will you make money in a desert?"

My younger sister called me later that week to tell me the cancer had returned. She asked if I could send more money. So, I started seeing guys I'd never usually see. One of them, a doctor, wrote me a prescription for tiny, oval-shaped pills that rolled all the secrets right off my skin, like water off of waxed hide. Every centavo went to Ma.

When Ana finally called it was a freak snow storm in spring. She told me she was getting married, and her voice sparkled like she'd done something bad and gotten away with it. I invited her over to drink her excitement away. Through the glass window of the building's door, I saw her waiting on the snowy stoop, looking like a lady who buys her clothes at department stores instead of thrift shops. Her tangled chocolate hair covered in flurry, bare hands flaunting a glistening diamond ring. She should've worn gloves on such a cold day. Even though it was the middle of April.

"Raquel!" Ana said throwing her arms over my shoulders. The icy flakes on her wool scarf melted against my cheek. "Where have you been?"

As happy as I was to see her again, something inside me, a small but well-armored door, slammed shut. I shuffled in slippers back towards my apartment. "Right here," I said. "But you have the exciting news."

Ana threw her coat over the arm chair by the radiator and held out her hand. "My Christmas present," she said. But all I could see were the shiny scars cross-hatched along her inner arm.

"Christmas present?" I said. "So you got engaged months ago. Everything must be going well." I headed to the refrigerator. "Want a beer? Or, I can mix a vodka something."

Ana pulled two bottles of sparkling wine from her purse. "This is a celebration, right?" She yanked out a cork, which shot off and smacked the ceiling. We sat around the wood table in the kitchen, next to the open window. I hadn't seen my wild thing for a few days. Her kibble sat untouched. I called out to her, worried that she'd froze to death. Wild thing! The only sound outside was the pat, pat of snow falling on more snow. Ana poured the pretty liquid into mugs. The bubbles puffed in applause.

I asked her about wedding plans.

"All we know for sure is that we're going to Cancún for our honeymoon," she said.

"Oh," I replied. "How's Jake's Spanish?"

Ana reached over to the open window and yanked it closed. "It's too cold in here."

"So how did this happen? Why Jake? I mean he's so—"

"Girl, I'm in love." Ana's eyes seemed suddenly vulnerable. "Can you believe it?"

I put down my mug of wine, ready to tell her everything. But my stomach knotted and my hands tingled with nerves. I reached into my purse, fingered around for an oval pill, found one, and swallowed it with my spit. As soon as it touched my tongue, I started to relax. "I have something you should try on." From my closet, I pulled out a black garment bag, and hooked it over the bathroom door. The dress is cut like a calla lily, simple, an immaculate white, embroidered with swanlike patterns.

"Que fancy," Ana said. "Where'd it come from?"

"Michael bought if for me."

I handed it to her; the weight felt satisfyingly heavy like a thick chain. She took the dress and it caught the sunlight from the window and glowed like something holy. Or maybe that was just the pill working.

"Who's Michael?"

I took another sip of wine and Ana wrestled off her tight blue jeans, flashing me a ludicrous pair of floral print undies. I scanned the back of her body for purple and blue signs of Jake's hands. I saw nothing. Michael had taken me shopping for an outfit to wear to dinner. I'd tried on that white dress and fell in love. All the sales guys asked if Michael and I were getting married, and he blushed like a bolo. I chose a pair of black stilettos to wear with it, but had to sell them when I came up short on rent one month. To me, they'd matched perfectly: The matte black and violent heel punctured the heart of the innocent dress.

Ana pulled the thin straps over her shoulders. I zipped her up, and the fabric sucked tight against her curves. She twisted her hair on top of her head, held it with one hand, the other posed on her hip. "Would you marry this?"

"Hell no," I smiled.

Ana stuck her tongue out, then made her face real serious. She walked barefoot across the hardwood floors toward the full-length mirror, like an enchanted girl in a story book. Like a bride. The mirror stands beside my desk, and I followed Ana there. The room smells musty in that corner, an inside smell. The sculpture I was working on then was a flying raccoon. Balanced on her hind legs, human-like paws groping in front of her as though sleep walking. I'd run a thick metal wire through the scavenger's back where eventually the wings would go. I made the wings myself from the feathers of four different birds: rusty brown turkey feathers, speckled quail, zebra- striped ewing, and dagger-red pheasant plumes.

Ana walked back to the table and popped the other bottle, white smoke curled around her hand.

"Ana," I said. "There's something I need to tell you." I imagined my body as it had been, half a life time ago. The tightly compressed knots of passion that sprang out like cactus flowers in spring. That day, it was spring and still snowing. "I'm a sex worker." I thought saying sex worker would make it sound like a white collar job.

She put on a dis-believing smile. "You're selling pupusa? Are you for real?"

I explained that I'd never be able to make my art and send money home if I wasn't *selling pupusa.* How actually, it's a great job with the exception of a few shitty guys.

"But at least I'm getting paid to deal with them," I said.

The air in the room suddenly went still. I told her the dress she had on was a gift from a client, she touched the fabric on her hips. "But it's so classy."

She tugged the zipper down and turned her back to me. But, I saw. On the thickest part of her thick brown thighs, scars piled in a lumpy keloid mess. Line upon line, some as wide as a finger, some as thin as a scalpel blade.

"Don't tell me Jake did that."

"I did." she said casually as she hung the dress back in the garment bag. "We all have our secrets."

I've seen her undressed a hundred times before, but right then her body felt like an extension of my own that had been amputated. A ghost limb. I reached out my hand to touch the scars. They were smooth. Topographical. An overgrown thicket of feeling. My skin tore from voice box to vulva, my insides crawled slowly onto my lap. I grabbed my bag and dug around for another white pill. I never took two. Especially after drinking.

"You started dating Jake too soon after Mauricio. I knew it was a bad idea."

She'd put her clothes back on, and sat in the arm chair tying her boots. She shook her head, and said nothing.

"Why Jake, Ana? I *know* guys like that."

I tried to stand but the room blurred. I steadied myself against the window, then flung it open. Fresh snow fluttered in.

"What's wrong with you?" Ana asked. "Where are you?"

"I know Jake," I said, settling myself back in the chair like the mess I was.

"You think you're funny, but actually you're fucked up. For real."

"It's true." I said, "Ask him."

"I'm out." I heard Ana's voice float around me, but she'd disappeared. Or maybe I had. It's ok. Everywhere, everyday, people, relationships, memories, they disappear. Maybe someday they emerge out of nothing, like they'd been there all along. Like they'd been sleeping and now they're awake. Like they were just waiting to be found. That night, I reappeared on the floor next to the kitchen table. Wild thing lay on my chest, her sharp claws grasping and contracting into my skin. She put her muzzle up to mine, yellow fangs bared, her soft breath tickled my nose.

"You ok?" I asked her. "I thought I'd lost you.

In July, Ma sent me a picture from the wedding. She'd been taking her mandatory walk on South Van Ness and seen the procession coming out of a church. Ana wore a shimmering ankle length dress with a beaded shawl across her shoulders. Her smiling idiot husband held her left arm and her stone-faced mother the right. Ma wrote, *You should have been there, hija. Dónde estás?* My cheek stung like I'd been slapped, again.

Months later, I ran into Ana on the street. We stopped and stared like we'd seen ghosts, before grabbing each other into a breathless hug. I told her about the picture. That she had looked happy on her wedding day. She shrugged and told me the news. Her mother had been contacted by her cuñada. Ana's father's remains were identified in an unmarked grave with the bodies of other resistance fighters. Her mother was traveling back to El Salvador for the first time since she left thirty years before.

"No shit," I said. "Aren't you going with her?"

"I can't get away," Ana replied. Then she asked me if I still planned to run away to the desert.

"Some day."

"Tell me when." She squeezed my arm. "I'll meet you there."

But the July night Ma sent me their wedding picture, I wasn't sure if I'd ever see Ana again. I tried the dress on. It glided over me with a sensual slickness, but the rigidity of the embroidery was armor-thick. I walked around the apartment on my tippy toes pretending to be a bride 'til I got bored. Early in May, I'd flushed all the pills down the toilet and tried sobriety on for size. It fit for a while. I drank two cups of black coffee, took the dress off and kicked it across the wood floor. Naked, in front of the mirror, I wondered at the outside of my body: brown eyes, black hairs, purple labia, amber skin. I saw beneath the skin too: The bald red muscles and the network of veins and organs. Everything, really, is beneath the skin.

I took the scalpel from my desk and sat at the kitchen table, set the cold, thin blade just below my elbow and pressed down. I felt the skin split before the electric shock of pain shot up my arm and around my skull. My head filled with a sound like metallic waves; my fingers pulled the blade towards my wrist for the length of an exhale. Blood slowly rose to the surface. I peered inside, wishing I could see all the pieces of Ana that are stitched into me. My wild thing purred at the window. She looked in with her huge eyes and walked delicately onto the table, tail swishing side to side. She sat long enough to know my secret, then turned around, hopped off the window ledge and into the night.

After Hurricane Sandy

Cynthia Dewi Oka

We climb toward the rumored grave
of an Native American healer, the earth
a vertigo of blackness and exposed
root beneath our palms, pressing up
through the waves of molten leaves,
toward the bluff where our children,
having for the past hour pretended
not to hear our demands for them
to come down, are now balancing
their sun-licked, baby-fat-all-but-gone
bodies, on a thin shelf of rock. "Look,
it's a deer! A deer in a wolf's face!"
their cries tumble down, snagging
like runaway rags on the branches;
they look like Brutus and Cassius
debating the fate and meaning of
a red stain the size of a man etched
into granite, commanding the speech
of minerals – they've found a myth
worth more than their mothers' fear.
The wind makes a bear of me, gristling
my chest and thighs as I crawl, gravity

inhaling me like an enormous throat,
over the deadness of trees and thorned
bushes, knuckles bursting like berries,
thoughts detritus around a New York
Post article I read about a woman, who
weeks ago, her brain sweaty with prayer,
climbed the rope of her body, her black
body, up the steepest mountain in America,
which rose between the door of her car
where her children rocked each other
in the arms of the storm, and the door
of the house she knocked and knocked,
until her knuckles burst into mouths,
her body a black tongue, a root burning
against which the family in the living room
drily surveyed their possessions:
fine china, paintings collected over
the years, utensils gleaming in candlelight,
the life-size television – their window
into loss and destruction – which
is silent now, their sleeping Noah.
The door did not open. The animals in
the house survived, while two baby boys
washed away, their screams became
the moulted skin of water as it bucked,
roiled against its own vanishing empire,
claiming for days a solid mass, blitzkrieg
of porches and tire swings, of libraries,
the vowels of a child's eyes looking up
at the body that broke open for him
and keeps breaking, like a faulty dam,

even after water returns to water, lifting
like souls in sunlight, to form the clouds
that now drift above us, waiting their turn
to kiss the mouth of a forgotten grave,
the red of a mother's heart. I hold my son
to me, I breathe him, and try to witness
the miracle of leaves still clinging
to branches, scrawling their petitions
on the November breeze – even as we
stare at our knuckles, the ripe strength
of them, on this precipice we have been
led to in the wake of the flood, asking
the gods, which do we raise them to be:
deer or wolf? The dead give nothing away.

A Hard Bed

Princess Perry

Nineteen year old Joh Pember careened down the center of Freeman Farm road spinning whorls of dust and spitting gravel. He wheeled the ten year old 1929 wood-sided Model A like it was stolen and new, like anything oncoming would give way. He was on the road to Clyde Adock's Feed and Seed to pick up corn for hogs he hated. Gluttonous beasts, they broke through the electric fence almost weekly. Always the one to fetch them, Joh found pigs in the peanuts or sweet potato mounds, rooting up a week's worth of sweat and backache. He drove them home with a stout club. If they dawdled, he landed a hard kick.

But that morning, the hogs were securely in their pen. Joh was alone in the truck and, with a little money in his pocket besides what he needed for feed, headed to town. The sun was shoulder-high over the drab and green fields, and as he swept past the light skated and slid, played coy and reappeared, a bright warm spot on the seat beside him, a slender beam bending across his face.

It was in that new-sprung, flirty light that Joh saw her, yellow skirt swinging around her brown muscled calves and bouncing up the back of her thighs as she jumped hopscotch. The sight of her hit him like his first drunk—a sweet, surprising, full-body flush—just like the half a bottle of communion wine, stolen when he was twelve years old. He forgot the near-empty feed troughs and that Namon, his older brother, had warned him what would happen if the hogs broke free again. He tooted the horn, a bright frivolous sound, and steered the truck to the side of the road.

"I know you," he said as he leaned out of the window, his red "PURE" motor oil cap matching his red and khaki checkered shirt. "Your mama sing in the choir. Y'all live down Blackrock. What you doing all the way out here?"

She nodded toward the bush of golden rod, just budding, flanking the path home. "I stay here now with my Aunt 'Melia. You Joh. How come you don't come to church no more?"

"Cause I didn't know you was out of nursery worshipping with the grown-folks," he said.

She smiled. "I bet you don't even remember my name, if you ever knowed it."

Joh turned his face to the windshield as if he might find her name magically there, then back to her, admitting, "You right, you right. I don't. But I'll pay for the privilege with a ride to wherever you going."

"School."

"School! You still in school? How old you?"

"Fifteen."

"Fifteen! Most folks I know *been* left school! You trying to learn it all, ain't you?"

"I'm gon' be a nurse."

"A colored nurse? 'Round here?"

"There's other places 'cept 'round here."

"Is there? Why don't you climb in here and tell me 'bout some of'em." He reached to the passenger side and loosened the wire that held the door shut.

"Thank you," she said, "I'll wait for the bus."

Joh shrugged, shut the door. "Suit yourself." He looked up the empty road. "Sometime the school bus come. Sometime it don't. Depends on if they got a full load of white. Depends on if they feel like driving down here."

"I got legs for more than hopscotch."

Joh smiled as he slid the gearshift into first. "That's what I know," he said. "That's what I know."

He came back any morning he and his brother worked separate corners of the farm and whenever Namon left the truck unattended. She traded her name, Molly, for sweet talk and bars of candy - almonds, coconut, chocolate—that had cost the biggest portion of Joh's spending change. But still it took weeks to get her into the truck, and weeks more before Molly abandoned her school books under the flowering cover of her aunt's lemon-gold hedge, and let Joh teach her all else those strong brown legs were good for.

***

Molly grasped the dashboard and tried to keep her seat as the truck bounced in and out of potholes. They were finally headed home, to the farm Joh and his brother owned. As the landscape had grown more and more familiar, they'd talked less and less. Miles ago, the complaints of the truck began to fill the space left by their voices. Molly scooted forward at the turn off to Aunt Amelia's, now flanked by the laden boughs of Bradford pear trees. A breeze volleyed the leaves like flags of welcome.

"We ought to live with your aunt," Joh said quietly.

Molly watched as the pear trees shrank then disappeared. The yearning in her gaze altered as it settled upon Joh. He looked small inside his blue, checkered shirt—narrow chest and charcoal skin, nineteen-years old—a skinny black boy, not a husband. But they were married. A letter signed by her mother. A half-hour at the courthouse. Afterward they drove to the Outer Banks. With no money for a room, they'd left Hargraves', the only place where coloreds could drink and dance, to sleep in the bed of the truck. Her honeymoon night, but Molly did not want to make love. Grudgingly, Joh let her be. But his hand, moist and heavy, settled against her bare belly. When he fell asleep, Molly rolled away.

"She ain't gon' want nothing to do with me for a while," Molly said. "You said your brother will let us stay."

"He will."

"Then why you talking 'bout living with Aunt 'Melia?"

Joh drew his lips tightly over his teeth as if to hold in a mouthful of things. He looked toward the road. "Namon gon' be mad I kept the truck, is all."

***

The house was stark. Wood, brick, glass. It was nothing like the home Molly left behind, Aunt Amelia's, where there were so many potted plants on the stoop it was hard to gain the door, and the yard burst with every flowering bush imaginable: royal purple hydrangea, lavender-pink Josee Lilacs, white-turned-golden fountain grass, the pale raspberry of Paree Peonies. In Joh and Namon's yard, there was not even the promise of a bud; even the grass had been chewed by the tire treads and buried in the ruts.

Joh cut the motor. Namon Pember, out front cleaving stove wood, waited with the ax hanging at his side. He was tall, hard-muscled, profoundly black. Up close, Molly found her new brother-in-law to be as severe as his house. He switched the ax from hand to hand. "Where you been?" he demanded.

"Out to Duck," Joh answered. "Hargraves. I'm married." Clipped words hid the quaver of his voice. Molly stopped herself in the act of reaching for Joh's hand.

"She gon' have a baby," Namon said flatly.

"Yeah."

Namon's gaze hardened as it moved from Joh's quaking bravado to Molly's shamed face.

"Goddamn!" he said, his words for both of them. "Goddamn if you ain't the stupidest–" Namon raised the ax high above his head and brought it arcing down. Biting wood chips flew at Joh and Molly.

They did not step back or even cover their faces. Defenseless, wordless, Molly and Joh stood guilty before Namon, less husband and wife than trembling children.

***

Molly watched dollops of sweetened cornmeal batter spread in hot lard as she stirred ham hocks, mustard greens and white potatoes with a splintered wood spoon. She heard Joh outside washing up at the pump. Namon already sat at the kitchen table. "You forgot the ice water," was all he'd said since walking through the door. His broad hand spread over *Pathways in Science and Learning About Our World*, a much mended schoolbook Molly had set aside to make supper. He pushed the pages back and forth. "Whenever I see your aunt down to the store, she bragging on you," he said. "She always saying how smart you is. How far you come in school. You ain't so smart after all, is you?"

Molly flipped the bread. She took a pitcher of water from the ice box and set it on the table. Her hands shook.

"What was you gon' be? A school teacher?"

"I's gon' be," Molly said, voice trembling like her hands, "a nurse."

"*Gon' be*? There was already three marks against you. Poor. Colored. Girl. Now you married. Gon' have a baby."

"Nothing to say I still can't be a nurse."

Namon snorted.

Joh rushed through the door with his cap off and his hair and face still damp. "It ain't on the plates yet, Molly?"

"Feed them hogs?" Namon asked.

"Joh, get my book," Molly said, as she turned toward the table with a plate in each hand.

Absently, Namon grabbed the book and dropped it to the floor. "You setting to this table and them hogs ain't ate?"

"I been -" Joh began to explain as the plates clattered to the table. Molly stooped to retrieve her fragile book. Dismayed and angry, she looked up at Namon.

"I got to take care 'a that! Miss Bond won't let me borrow no more if I tear it up!"

"What you need a book for?" Namon asked as he pulled a plate forward.

"I'm going back."

Again, Namon snorted. He turned to Joh. "What I tell you gon' happen if them hogs get out again?"

Molly stood. "Ain't I going back to school, Joh?"

Joh looked from his brother to his wife. He pulled a plate forward. "Hush, Molly," he said.

"Ain't that what we said?"

"Hush!" Joh ordered. "I can't taste my food for all this foolishness!"

Molly took a step toward Joh. "We said -"

"School is out," Namon spoke firmly. "What you look like sitting up in a school room full of children when you got one in your belly? You married now. There's work for you 'round here." He picked up his fork.

Standing beside the table, Molly clutched her book. She watched Namon and Joh bend their heads over greens she had picked clean and boiled. Their white teeth tore her cornbread. They chewed and drank and swallowed as if the matter were settled.

***

Namon Pember waited in Clyde Adock's store to buy a pack of Chesterfields. He stood aside at the long wood and glass counter while Adock talked to Roy Gilliam, an extension agent and a sometime cotton-ginner. It was Roy's job to travel Bertie County, bringing word of better farm equipment and pest control to farmers. Somehow, though, he never managed to make it to the coloreds and poor whites. In harvest season, when farmers had little time or attention to spare, Gilliam once in a while ginned cotton, his skillful extra hands allowing the overrun gin owner to stretch the workday from early morning until late in the night.

Commonplace except for his job, Gilliam was born of the peasant farmers who bartered and sold at Adock's. Nowadays, with a buzz cut that showed a clean pink scalp and starched khaki shirts with "*Gilliam*" sewn in heavy grade, dark blue thread over the breast pocket, he was better off. Still, on his rounds from big farm to big farm, he always stopped at Adock's for the time it took to win a game of checkers and drink a beer.

At the counter, he debated crop quotas and government price supports, brushing off Adock's reluctance to argue and efforts to wait on Namon. The checker players got fed up. "Gilliam!" one called, "I got a crop to bring in in 'bout three months. You be ready to play by then?"

Gilliam slapped the counter. "You gon' see, Clyde!" he said backing away. "You gon' see that Roosevelt ain't nothing but one 'a them socialists!" He took another step and his heel clipped an open bag of feed. "Damn it!" he said, as he looked down at the flow of spilled grain. Then, as easy as shoving a suitcase at a bellhop, he gestured to Namon, "Pick that up."

Clyde Adock was already coming from behind the counter with a dust pan and broom. "I got it, Roy."

"He'll get it," Roy said as he reached deep into a barrel of ice for a bottle of beer.

Namon stood stiff as a cooling board. This was not his first run in with a man like Gilliam. It wasn't his second. Perhaps Namon understood better than Roy Gilliam himself why he so despised colored people and beggared whites. Gilliam was all but one of them. A favor or a phone call from a rich white man, and Gilliam had been lifted from the status of poor white trash. Now he had a job that put him on speaking terms with men of historic names and Confederate deeds. They might offer him a whiskey or a cigar in return for exclusive information. But he had the same chance as Namon to sit at their tables or be introduced to their daughters. Namon said, "I wasn't nowhere near that bag."

With his hand on the cap of the amber glass bottle, Roy Gilliam tensed.

There rose in the store the atmosphere of a cockfight - strutting, speckled birds with razors fastened to their feet—calming only when one rooster tore the head from another. Clyde Adock surveyed the room. The white men who played checkers and ate sardines and cheese in his store had a lot in common with Namon Pember. Their farms were always at the mercy of animal disease and crop blight. Like Namon, they were passed over for loans while big acreage "farmers" who rarely touched dirt reaped subsidy checks. All in the same leaky boat, Adock had extended credit to every one of them to a man. Sometimes they called this to mind. Adock had seen them trade remedies, tools, and sometimes a cigarette with Namon. Yet these were the years of Scottsboro, when good white citizens marveled that a gang of black boys jailed for raping white women had lived long enough to deny it in court. They straightened from the board. The gaze of every white man was on Namon, and Adock. Gilliam's hand slid down the neck of the unopened bottle. He gripped it like a hammer.

"Roy," Adock said, "there ain't got to be none of that. Namon gon' do what I say. How he gon' feed his animals and fertilize his cotton he don't?" Adock spoke coldly to Namon, "Nobody asked where you was. Do what he said."

Namon scanned the room. The only other colored in the store was Irving, the thirty-five year old stock "boy." High up on a ladder, dusting the red labeled cans of mackerel, he didn't even look down. There were five whites. Adock wouldn't pile on, but Irving wouldn't help. Namon had a new crop in the field. He couldn't work if they beat him badly. Joh could not do the work alone.

On knees that bent as if they were bit by bit breaking, Namon knelt and scraped the floor clean. But before he did, he looked into the eyes of Roy Gilliam—as if he were not outnumbered and surrounded–with the white-hot fury of any other man.

***

With a hand still coated in grain dust and floor grit Namon reached into his shirt pocket for a cigarette. Nothing.

"Goddamn!" he said, bringing his attention back to the road just as a sow and three shoats trotted across. He slammed the truck to a stop, fishtailing in the road.

As fast as the truck and the narrow dirt lane would let him, Namon sped home. He found his brother in the hog pen kneeling among the slack fencing. Just as Joh looked over his shoulder to explain, Namon drew back his foot. Full weight and full of rage, he kicked Joh.

"Find," he said, "those goddamned pigs."

***

Molly's Aunt Amelia squatted by a whitewashed tractor tire filled with dirt. She was setting out the plant clippings that usually crowded her window sills. Beneath a fraying straw hat, she hummed "The Old Sheep Know the Road," breaking her melody only to murmur, "Root for me now, hear?" as she lifted plants from jars, tangled roots dripping, and arranged them in the soil. Around each plant she poured murky water from its own jar so the strange new home would feel familiar.

"*Aunt 'Melia*," Molly said.

Her name spoken in a misery voice, and Amelia was yanked from her only peace. She studied her full hands for the briefest moment, then look up. "Well, what happened?"

"I ain't going back to school."

Amelia studied the girl's woeful expression. This was news, it seemed, but only to Molly. "Why?"

"Joh's brother say I can't."

"What Joh say?"

"Nothing."

Amelia studied the hydrangea cuttings, then gazed about her yard. In some patches and corners, weeds had gotten ahead of her flowers. Amelia kept gardens for a few women in Windsor whose husbands were still wealthy enough to pay, and she came home in the evenings with her back aching and her inspiration spent. She was late putting her own garden into the ground. Maybe the plants would root and she'd have "snowballs" bordering the walk to her privy, their white petals carpeting the ground. But all of this could be for nothing. Thrive or shrivel. One was just as likely as the other. So it was with this girl. All of that hard work and hope gone to nothing.

When Molly said she wanted to be a nurse, Amelia had begun holding back a portion of her tithes to pay for schooling. She had envisioned introducing the girl, "This my niece. She a nurse," meaning, "She educated. You can't do her like you do me." Now she understood the enormity of her sin, the arrogance of her dream. When Molly turned up pregnant, Amelia said, "That's what come of robbing God."

"Aunt 'Melia?"

"I said don't let that boy turn your head." Amelia gouged a hole in the dirt. "Go to school. Get your lesson. You wouldn't listen. You wanted to be *grown*. Thought you was grown when you was sneaking off with that boy. *That* didn't make you no woman." She paused. She could almost see the rebuke, the reality, spreading through the girl like that dark water taken up by the roots. "What you feeling right now," Amelia said sadly, "*that* make you woman."

Molly finally spoke, her voice diminished like the third sounding of an echo. "What am I gon' do?"

Amelia might have told the girl to go home to her Ma, but there were still four hungry mouths to feed at Odell's. Molly's mama didn't need a grown girl coming back with a baby. She might have, again, taken Molly, but hard times were turning desperate. City whites were moving back to take field jobs, and what they didn't take, cotton picking machines did. Hoot, her husband, hadn't worked steady in weeks, and weeks were all it took for the notes on the stove and furniture to fall behind. Amelia's cupboards were not bare, but she and Hoot had little in abundance. Molly had a husband who owned part of the land he farmed. Two men to plow and harvest and hunt for food if it came to that. She had to stay, hard bed and all.

"*Aunt 'Melia?*"

Chest deep, Amelia sighed. "Go home," she said. "That's what you gon' do. A woman with a child don't leave home over nothing like that."

Amelia let Molly sit and weep as she quickly set out the rest of her cuttings, the joy of planting gone, the fancy arrangements forgotten.

***

Joh came home from the hog pen to find Molly asleep at the kitchen table, head on folded arms. Her book lay open in front of her. The stove was cold. The skillet from breakfast sat unwashed. Plates, frosted with grease, waited in cold dishwater. He shook Molly until she waked.

"This what you been doing?"

She raised her head and looked around as if she expected to wake in a different place. Gradually, her features settled. "I went to Aunt "Melia's," Molly mumbled.

"An left the house like this? An come back an come back an ain't fix supper?"

"I come back in time," she said, defensively, rising awkwardly, her body still adjusting to the weight and ride of the baby. "I was just tired, I guess, from the walk."

"Ain't too tired to put your eyes in that book."

"What my book got to do with anything?" Molly snapped. "You hungry, I'll get you something. Gon' wash."

Joh came in from the pump to find leftover hominy and ham warming in the skillet, but the breakfast dishes were still in the pan. Molly sat at the table, her fingers skimming over pages.

"You ain't wash that frying pan," Joh said.

Molly shrugged. "Bacon grease is bacon grease."

From the backdoor, Joh reached her in three strides. His fist hit her book like a hard swung bat, knocking it to the floor, shattering the rotten thread of the binding.

"What's wrong with you!" Molly screamed.

She threw herself down, stooping and squatting, gathering the strewn leaves. Joh raised his foot.

He stomped near Molly's fingers, near her face, until she crouched on her haunches; only her bewildered gaze followed Joh. Dirt and hog shit from the tread of his boot smeared the pages, imprinted a chapter deep. He ground his heel until layers of pages ripped.

"Now!" Joh yelled as he stood over Molly. "Tend to something!

***

Namon arrived not long after Joh stalked back to the fields. He came upon Molly as she stood by the stove staring down at her belly with an expression too fierce to be love.

"How come you looking at it that way?" he asked.

"What way?" Molly asked. "I ain't looking at it no kinda way." She made up her face like she made up the beds. Folded and tucked. Neat around the edges.

"You ain't so dumb after all, is you?"

"Hominy and ham all there is for supper," Molly said.

"Dish it up then." Namon approached the table. Her book lay there, pieced together, even the shit-covered pages. "Book don't look so precious today," he said, flicking it with one finger.

"Leave it 'lone, please."

Namon withdrew his hand. "What got hold to it?"

"Joh."

"What for?"

"Hateful!" Molly teared as she asked in a quieter voice, "What it hurt yall if I read my book and go to school?"

Namon gripped the back of a chair. He only knew that all of her talk of going to school caused a desperate anger to well in him. It was a filthy feeling, like when a pounding rain caused the outhouse to flood and run over, but he could not help it.

"That ain't your place." He sat at the table, waiting for Molly to bring his plate.

Instead of spooning grits and ham onto a plate, Molly stared at Namon. He stared back. Between them was the same feeling that had risen in Adock's store. The tension felt like the moment just before the cocks were released.

"It moved," Molly said. "I was looking at it that way 'cause it moved."

***

For two days and nights, Molly and Joh performed the obligations of marriage—he brought in stove wood, Molly cooked his breakfast—but little else passed between them. On the third night, Joh dropped heavily onto his side of the bed. He shucked off his shirt. His back was stamped with a spreading bruise, less apparent because of his dark skin, but painful. Stiffly, he bent to unlace his boots. Molly turned her miserable face to his injured back.

The boy into whose truck she'd climbed was not this boy. That Joh had been a charming thing, a slim dark boy with a sly, easy smile. She likened him to something beautifully wild slipping through the woods. Molly had meant to go only close enough to take a look. One day, she left her books beneath a covering of flowers. Then another day, then another, never imagining she would not make it back.

Joh worked the ties on his boots. "Namon say he gon' get a second-hand tractor if we make a good crop. He do, he won't need me so much." One boot hit the floor with a thud. "We could leave here."

Molly rose onto her elbow. "Go where?"

"Virginia. Newport News. I might could get on at the shipyard."

"A big colored hospital's there. Whitaker Memorial."

"I know," Joh said.

He put out the light and crawled into bed. Molly lay back against her pillow. Neither slept.

After a while, Joh asked, "You feeling all right?"

Molly answered, "I'm feeling all right."

***

Amelia brought baby clothes, cut and stitched by her own hands, diapers with sharp shiny pins, and a cradle mended and varnished. When she left, Molly pushed everything beneath her bed, out of sight. She felt the anticipation and fear of an expectant mother only for Namon's crop.

For this, she put her book away. Like Namon, she examined the soil and watched the weather. Without being asked or told, she worked the fields, squatting, bending, weeding on the days when squares nubbed the young stems and when those squares split into buttery flowers. Molly gathered the fallen blossoms in each of their short lived stages, purple-tipped, then pink and red, and saved them like first teeth, like locks of hair.

Early in the season, when the first trembling, sunlit-green stand of cotton appeared, Namon set Joh and Molly to thinning out the plants. The task was simple. Where the seed bunched together, the new plants were to be dug out of the earth and resettled ten inches apart. Namon trusted Joh, but he kept close watch on Molly, finally leaving his own rows for hers. "Not so rough!" he ordered as he knelt beside her in a furrow.

Namon snatched the dented and rusted spade from Molly's hand, but with seedlings he was tender. He dug a circle around a clump of plants, mindful of roots, and untangled them like a finger smoothing a wild brow. Molly noticed his hands—scarred from plow lines and wire punctures—coarse hands moving cautiously, not only, she suspected, because there was money at stake.

"You love this work."

Absorbed, so unguarded, Namon grunted, "Yeah."

Molly touched the miniature, hand-shaped leaf of a cotton seedling. She took a delicate stem between thumb and forefinger.

"I could rip it up," she said, "the way Joh done my book."

She saw Namon's dismay before his face sealed in anger. Namon stood, but Molly held his gaze.

"I feel like that about school."

"Just do like I say," he ordered. He moved many rows away from her.

Molly knelt in the dirt, stretching beyond her growing belly, ignoring the low ache in her back. She worked the plants just as Namon had shown her, cautious with the fragile roots, each plant, in her mind, a separate page.

***

Over the months of summer, Molly followed the men, chopping weeds that came up faster than cotton, always alert for weevils. One day, Joh ordered Molly home when he found her pacing the rows shaking poison from a thinly woven croaker sack onto the leaves. White dust enclosed her.

Joh pulled her to the edge of the field. "Don't you care *nothing* 'bout this baby?"

"Weevils eat the cotton, we can't leave," she said firmly.

Molly had taken to heart words that Joh wanted to take back. In the time it took for bruises to fade—blood reabsorbed into blood - Joh had forgiven Namon. Not many days after Namon kicked Joh, he came confiding the dream of a second-hand tractor. "You good with machine things," Namon said, "when it break, you'll fix it." *Sorry*—the only way Namon knew to say it.

Joh found himself trapped between the hard hopes of Namon and Molly. He pretended that he could serve them both. He did nothing to discourage Namon who planned an easier and more prosperous future with two men and a tractor. And Joh did not caution Molly who, in her ninth month, September, when cotton lint burst the bolls, looped a sack around her chest and headed to the fields.

***

The ginnery, like most vital things, was located at a crossroads. It was not modern - a mule-driven holdover from the last century - but the only gin that Namon and other small farmers could afford. It sat directly across from the firehouse and cater-cornered to the large general store where people bought gasoline and groceries, but traded news and gossip for free. On the other side of the road was the ball field. Some Saturdays white men played, and some Saturdays colored men played. Colored or white, the women cooked. They sold pulled pork barbecue, fried fish with white bread, white potatoes fried with onions, and grape or orange Nehi. Small children scrambled underfoot while the women wiped sweat and fishy grease from their faces, too busy to hear the calls of umpire or enjoy the play.

But there were no games during cotton harvest. The playing field was overrun with wagons and trucks and trailers pulled by Rumley and Model-D John Deere tractors, as the local farmers waited to have their upland cotton ginned. The wait was many things: long and thirsty if a man had used up his credit at the store; tense with a season's work piled in one place; worrisome with each man comparing quantity, texture, color, praying for a good grade, a high price.

Namon knew he had quality cotton. He had begun with high caliber, short staple cottonseed and picked only the ready bolls. He'd cautioned and badgered and eyed Joh and Molly to make sure they did the same. Once picking was done, Namon minded the cotton personally, sleeping but a little, taking care that the seed did not over-dry, trusting Joh to check the lint only a handful of times. Now, as Namon waited in line, he tried not to think how little any of that mattered. The quality of his cotton was determined as much by the vigilance of the ginner as it was by anything Namon had done while his crop was in the ground. The ginner's job was to take utmost care with how the cottonseed was pulled through the saws, grates and brushes. If he allowed the machine to jam or even looked away as the saws drew the cotton though the grate, knots could form in the fiber. A year of work could be greatly diminished or even lost.

Namon arrived to find farmers already waiting. Wagons and tractors rolled forward slowly until, a couple of hours before sundown, Namon stood on the slatted floor of the ginnery, his cotton mounded around his feet. Around him, the dark faces of women who moted cotton were softened by the gauzy haze of floating lint. Their talk of children, in-laws, and men revolved slowly in the humid evening air. In soft, ashy voices, they called to the barefoot colored boys who hung around the gin, running errands for pennies, and offered them nickels or paper money damp with bosom-sweat to fetch Coca-Colas and peanut butter crackers. The marriageable women aimed flirtatious looks at Namon. But one woman, older, with fingers that picked trash from the fiber faster and more deftly than the rest, did not aim to seduce. Her gaze traveled pointedly to the ginner who mounted the stairs.

Roy Gilliam crossed the gin house floor and stood in front of the cotton gin machine like a concert pianist. He nudged a mound of cotton with his boot. With a quick check of the belts and wheels, he glanced around for the farmer.

Namon stepped out of the shadow of a low-hanging, slanting beam. He kept his face expressionless; Roy Gilliam did the same, but they recognized each other. Their eyes, like glittering grindstones, gave them away.

Almost casually Gilliam asked, "You by yourself?"

"Yes, sir," Namon said.

"Adock ain't sent you?"

"No, sir."

Lifting the cotton, measuring by feel, loading the machine, Gilliam said, "I thought he'd sent you."

"No, sir," Namon repeated, each *sir* feeling like a lit cigarette stubbed on his skin.

Gilliam kept close watch on his hands, filling the machine with dirty seed cotton. His tone was no different than if he said, *sure is hot today*. "I thought you was his boy. The way you cleaned his floor, I thought you was his boy. Ain't you?"

Gilliam spoke loudly, but the moters pretended not to hear. An impatient cotton farmer, come inside to escape the mosquitoes and wait his turn, cocked his head to listen.

Namon glanced at the woman on the floor. Her fingers moved quickly and surely through the cotton lint. She did not look at him, but she did not have to. *Yes,* she would say. *Put a roof over your head. Put food on your table.* Put a tractor in your field. Put money away in case Joh's new baby takes sick.

Namon knew the words and posture that would get his cotton ginned to perfection. Grade A. Top price. He lowered his gaze to Roy Gilliam's collarbone. In the humblest voice possible for a man of Namon's size and ambition, he said, "*Yas, sir.*" The words tore from his throat like a ribbon of flesh.

Gilliam inhaled. He nodded. "I knew you was," he said. "I knew you was."

He fed and adjusted the machine. The teeth grabbed the first bolls. Seeds rolled down the grate.

Though he saw the parts move, Namon was oblivious to the din of the saws and the rattle of the housing and gears. The approving nod from the woman was incomprehensible. Only shame reached him, humiliation so dense, it felt as if he'd crawled inside a cotton bale.

But as he watched, clean lint fell over the brushes; he forced out his hand. Namon clutched one fistful of seed-free, Grade A cotton before Roy Gilliam said, "Got to feed the mules."

He sent the owner's son, a boy of sixteen or seventeen, to gin

Namon's cotton. Downstairs, Roy Gilliam smoked a cigarette as he watched the mules—hungry, dumb, obedient—churn in the track, and the gin chewed Namon Pember's cotton.

***

Hardly able to sleep for her own excitement and the baby stretching and curling within her, Molly woke instantly at the sound of the knocking truck motor. She shook Joh.

"Namon's back!" she said, throwing off the sheet and maneuvering her legs over the side of the bed.

Joh pressed his face into the pillow. "In the morning," he mumbled.

"This can't wait 'til morning." Molly grabbed her dress from a hanger behind the door. "Joh! Get up!"

She stood by the window tugging on her dress. Nothing outdoors moved as excitedly. Grass and leaf-laden branches swayed. Some small vulnerable animal crept into a weed-clump near the shed. Only Molly and sleepless whippoorwills disturbed the night. She scanned the long trails of moonlight until she found Namon's shadow. He sat motionless on the tailgate. He did not honk the horn or bellow for Joh to help carry cotton seed to the shed. He did not stomp through the house, rousting Molly out of bed to cook hot food on the night he'd sold his best cotton crop. Namon sat straight and still like the grief-stricken sit at funerals, as if minding heartbeat, breath and thought, anything that could race away and burst from him as screams. Molly sat that way one time, the day she understood she was pregnant.

Just over her shoulder, Joh heaved a months-old sigh. He stood in shorts and long-toed bare feet, thin chest and arms as wiry as his hair. Slowly, Molly took her hands from the buttons of her dress and turned to better see him. His face softened, caved like the center of a cake. They saw the same thing: There would be no shipyard job in Newport News, no training at Whitaker; he would not be blamed.

"There ain't gon' be no tractor," he said. "We ain't leaving."

In a voice like skin splitting, Molly asked, "Why didn't you let me alone? That first day? I *told* you—"

Joh, a stick-and-stuffed scarecrow limned by the moonlight, shrugged his shoulders. "I thought you'd let go of the notion."

***

Namon softly spoke, "Go inside, you know what's good for you."

Molly ignored him. She heaved onto the tailgate.

They sat together in the churl of unseen frogs, the sound lingering, vacant. Separately, their gazes found, again and again, the moon-flooded field of withering stalks.

After a long while, Namon lifted his hand, trembling, and rested it on Molly's belly.

Sometime before daybreak, Molly pressed her hands upon his.

Backwards Through the Story

Audrey M. Peterson

I'm going to go backwards through this particular part of my story because I hate to end on a sad note. So that would place my friend John and me in 2005 in a small churchyard on Route 30 in Barbour County, Alabama somewhere between Clayton and Eufaula, from where we had just come. Mid-July and we're standing in a patch of shade at the back of the church, the only relief available, it being three o'clock p.m. in the sunny damn hot south.

We're in this yard because of a man named Peterson, Lyndon Peterson. We met him not a half-hour before in Eufaula. We met him because his name is Peterson and so is mine, his kinfolk are from those parts, and so are mine. I mentioned I was looking for this church, the Pleasant Grove Baptist Church, did he know where it was and did he know about the lynching there of a young man named Peterson way back when? He said he did, that his mama knew about it too because she attended that church. Everybody in the church knew about it, even knew which tree the lynchers used, only you won't find anything but the stump there now.

I'm going to get the hard stuff out of the way first. The Peterson boy—I call him the Peterson boy because his first name has been lost in the telling—was a young black man who lived on the high bluffs of Eufaula, right on its vast lake, where other coloreds lived. Every evening he'd go to fetch his girlfriend, who worked for a white family in town.

One of those nights he went to get his girl, her last name was Hegley, her first name lost, too. The street was dark, it had no lamps. The door opened and someone came out; the Peterson boy thought it was Miss Hegley and stepped forward saying "Here I am." But it was a white girl. I'm sure the white girl was just taken by surprise because it was dark. And she probably carried what happened next in her heart until the day she died. She screamed.

She screamed and the Peterson boy, scared himself, ran away, which could have been the end of it because she was not molested in any way. But the white citizens of Eufaula couldn't let it go. They interrogated and badgered the black population nonstop, until the Hegley girl, to her undying horror and regret, mentioned that her boyfriend came to pick her up at the spot of the encounter every night. They got up a posse, grabbed the boy from his home on the high bluffs, tied him behind a wagon, dragged him through the streets of Eufaula, castrated him, hung him on an oak tree near the church, and shot him.

A *New York Times* clipping reports that an Iver Peterson, 18, was lynched in Eufaula on February 12, 1911. That's got to be my Peterson boy. This deed lived in the same century as I lived. This deed has breathed the same air I have breathed. You may well ask me why I care. It's because he had a first name that was almost lost. Because he shares my name, so I own this.

Lyndon Peterson told it right. There was a church, a simple brick building with a white clapboard steeple and a sign that said Pleasant Grove Missionary Baptist Church. In back there was a small graveyard, full of scorched grass. And there was a stump in the yard near the church. There were other trees, including a big oak tree some yards away, but it was the stump that belonged to the hanging tree, according to the tale.

I was glad there was only a stump. I didn't want that oak there, intact. I didn't want to look into the branches of such a tree, unwitting as it might be of its role in the lynching. A tree is supposed to be about life, not death. I wondered if it died naturally, of a disease, or if it was struck by lightning, or if someone decided to cut it down, a tree nourished on the blood of a long-ago boy who may or may not be related to me. If his blood is my blood, then perhaps my blood was in that tree. A tree perhaps the congregation could not suffer to live.

The stump is the right place to say a prayer to the soul of the Peterson boy, nothing else. John takes photos, is horrified at the same time, shaking his head and shooting. There is an anger so deep you stop feeling it for a moment, and when it returns, it burns so bad from the inside out you want to peel off your skin to escape your body. But you can't. I felt that way by that stump—400-something damn years of this shit. This world doesn't deserve black people.

John is a white Latino, still I am comforted by his presence; he sees what I see and he understands. He stops shooting and I stand in front of him as if he can block all that sun. Even at six feet tall he is not nearly tall enough. The sun bakes the yard into a paralysis. The air doesn't move. Nor the walking stick, or beetle, or the snake in the grass, all still. The superheated silence of the churchyard becomes more awful than the vision of a castrated man hanging from a tree. We stand for a minute more, listening to the occasional passing car until the church and the sad little graveyard behind it become too much for us.

Besides, John is ready for barbecue. It's Thursday and in three days of traveling around he's yet to have any—a true crime considering where we are. Strange how, when faced with death we scramble to prove to ourselves that we're alive, and nothing says I'm alive like stuffing yourself with pork butt. "I've had enough of this," I say. We quit the yard, jump into the car and peel out.

Back in Eufaula, John had spotted a likely lunch spot. That was right after our visit with Dr. Moses Marcus Jones. Dr. Jones had been the last stop on a one-day tour of Eufaula. I had seen everything I had come to see for my research on the Peterson boy and was taking one last look at the tour brochure, when on the back page I saw site number 61 Milton-Moses M. Jones, MD.

"Wait!" I said. "Stop!" We were pulling out of Eufaula, about to go back over the bridge north. I was looking to take John to my grandfather's land. Peterson land. Battle land. That would be the grand finale of the trip South. "Moses Marcus Jones, M-M-Moses Marcus Jones." I could barely get it out of my mouth because I was so shocked at my own near miss. I had planned this trip so carefully, how could I have not thought to look this man up? He was the cousin of David Frost, Jr., the man who wrote the book, *Witness to Injustice*, in which I first read about the Peterson boy lynching. I had spoken to Dr. Jones over the phone two years earlier, looking for information. He promised to help me in any way he could.

We parked; I got out and walked in. Dr. Jones's practice was as old-fashioned as can be. There was a reception desk with a nurse and a receptionist and a waiting room with worn furniture, a few posters about diabetes and the like. Across the room was a sign with a large black "N" and a red circle with a slash through it. "Guess what that means?" John said five minutes later as he waited with me for Dr. Jones. I look at his rueful face and I didn't want to say.

"Miss Peterson?" I turn and there he is, a warm-looking man in his late fifties wearing a doctor's coat and gold-rimmed spectacles. "Why are you here?" he asks. He is smiling.

I explain that it was about the Peterson boy and Dr. Jones is on the phone calling every Peterson he knows within a twenty-mile radius. We talk about the book, and his practice, history, family trees. I tell Dr. Jones that before we were Petersons we were Battles, my great-great-grandfather was Amos Battle, and that my people lived and still live in the Battle Community the next county over. Dr. Jones knows the Battles too, his nurse, very tall, a warrior queen in some other life, is a Battle. Dr. Jones tells us he knew a Battle woman who told him if she took him into the woods on Battle land in the afternoon and they went deep enough, it would be just like midnight. That's how deep it is. That's how much land there is.

"And I believe her, too," he says.

Dr. Jones has occupied the 1850 Italianate style cottage that we're standing in for nearly 30 years, but you wouldn't know that from the brochure. In the Eufaula Heritage Trail brochure we learn about the architect of Dr. Jones's house, and the unusual octagonal chimney, but not that Dr. Jones was the rare black resident in a relentlessly white town, and even rarer, a black physician. We are just about to leave when a Peterson, Lyndon Peterson, shows up and I mention that I'd like to go to Pleasant Grove Baptist, and well, you know the rest.

"By the way, that sign with the "N" on it means no narcotics; I took a closer look. They put those signs up so junkies don't break in to steal dope," I tell John as we drive to the church, although I could bet that he thought it meant the use of the word "nigger" was strictly forbidden on those premises. I can't blame him—it was the first thing that sprung to mind when he pointed it out to me, both of us stuck in a time and place that would require such a sign. Never mind that Dr. Jones's last patient that afternoon was the frailest, whitest old lady, so white her veins were a delicate pattern of blue tracework over her face and hands. She was old enough to remember Jim Crow, and lived long enough to forget it. And she was thanking that colored doctor like he just gave her the secret of eternal youth.

Still, the only other black person I had seen so far in Eufaula besides Dr. Jones, his nurse, and Lyndon Peterson, was an old man sitting on his porch just at the south end of a street called Riverside Drive. What I saw was a very black man staring at us from the porch of his brokedown wooden house. Weeks later John would remind me that the man had no legs and was sitting in a wheelchair. This is where our stories go off in two directions, at the missing legs. I didn't see that his legs were gone, just a very black man's impassive face. John saw his stumps.

I was keen on seeing the Shorter Cemetery, one of two in Eufaula I had on my to-do list. There were some gravestones I needed to read, possibly those of one of the lynchers. So we rolled down Riverside Drive; glimpses of blue-blue Lake Eufaula peeked through a screen of trees to one side only yards away, while dusty, sleepy homes sat on our other side. The name of the drive, promising views and elegance but giving us neither, was a dead end. There was a sign saying we had found the cemetery, but the gate was locked up and chained. Behind the gate we could see a lane and trees and high grass. That's when I looked to my right and saw the old black man. He was offering no assistance. Just sat on his porch at the end of the lane and stared.

We turned around and as we were driving out someone was driving in. He was a white man, with a buzz cut. Oh hell, he was one boll of cotton away from singing "Dixie" as far as I was concerned. He stopped, so John stopped.

It's here I should explain that we were driving around in a red Sebring convertible, which I guess is unusual for those parts because we were gawked at and questioned wherever we went. Yet drive around in a bright purple Charger with spinning rims and nobody thinks it's strange.

"What're you people trying to do?" the man asks. Now I'm sure John will disagree with me, but I know I heard "you people" and that's all I needed to hear. While John is talking, explaining that we'd like to see the cemetery, I'm looking at this man, and in my head am daring him to look at me the wrong way. At the moment there is no difference between my mouth and my .357 Smith and Wesson when it is loaded and cocked. Not a bit of difference. He's looking at us a bit longer than he has to, and I see in his eyes that he's thinking.

(Think before you speak, think before you speak, think before you speak, cracker, think before you speak, oh please, I pray you think before you speak. Because you know, and I know that if you don't start none, won't be none. The world has spun around 385,440 times since I was born in 1962, and many things have changed, and if I have to go to that special circle in hell to channel my ex-Nazi grandfather to get the anger and evil I'll need to remind you that we done left the plantation—oh, I will.)

All the man says is "I guess there's a lot of history there, it's worth visiting."

(Thank you thank you thank you thank you white man from the South thank you.)

He gives the convertible the once over. "But you won't, naw you can't, you can't go, you won't make it in that car. Then again you could get out and crawl through the holes in the fence and walk down, the cemetery's in the woods, but then there's the snakes in the underbrush; it's pretty overgrown."

We decide to leave Eufaula.

Eufaula. It is a town I once only knew because any letters sent to my dad's people in Battle went to the post office in Eufaula, there being no post office in the colored community. Now it is a place of paradox, of knowing what happened there, and seeing what I see, of reconciling that terrible thing in the churchyard to the smiling blue-haired old ladies in the Eufaula Carnegie Library who couldn't have been nicer when I asked them about the town's genealogical records.

It wasn't a fluke. EVERYBODY was nice. Even the son of Dixie didn't have to stop and help us, but he did. The only truly mean person I encounter the five days I was in Alabama was a black girl working at a Stop-n-Shop, who glared at me while I served myself an ICEE. She must have been having a bad day. Or she could just have been one of those mean girls you hear about from up north, up my way. And try as I might, I still only saw about three Confederate flags in 2005, the same amount I saw on two earlier trips to Alabama. Of course we were three years away from a black president, and "negroes" not remembering their place.

We're on the self-guided tour of Eufaula and I'm having a hard time evoking the Eufaula of the antebellum even while sitting in front of a neoclassical revival mansion that looks like any minute somebody in a hoop skirt is going to burst out of it and drop to the ground with the vapors. I'm sitting in the car watching the mansion shimmer in the heat. John jumps out and takes some photos and we practically speed by the Couric-Smith home on our way to somewhere, anywhere inside and icy cool.

If you recognize the first part of the name, it is because the big white colonnaded house used to belong to Katie Couric's great great grandfather, a Frenchman who became a rich cotton merchant. He had slaves. Katie Couric's people had slaves. She never said it in that broadcast, but it had to be so. Hell, John's people on his father's side, dyed-in-the-wool Confederates from Arkansas, had slaves, too. I don't blame John for his great grands, no more than I take the blame that my grandfather was an SS officer. Levels the playing field. Skeletons are like that.

During a broadcast years ago, members of the *Today Show* team researched their genealogy and during her segment Katie mumbled something about a well-tended slave cemetery being nearby. She was standing in front of the very mansion that sits baking on a silent avenue of mansions, all preserved thanks to the quick thinking of the prominent citizens of Eufaula. Having heard that the South had lost the war, someone ran out waving a white flag to the Union army, who had not heard the war was over and was preparing to burn the town down. The troops moved on and the Union officers had dinner with the mayor. "Eufaula remained intact, her people unharmed," the walking tour brochure says. "Following the war, the town's fortunes suffered from the loss of plantation-produced cotton and Reconstruction." The darkies ran away and left us high and dry is what I want to add to that brochure, for clarification.

The well-tended slave graveyard was not so close to the mansion. It was in the Fairfield Cemetery a few blocks away from the Couric home, where Katie's grandparents are buried. John and I were in that cemetery earlier, before we started the tour. I wasn't looking for Petersons. I was looking for the memorials of "faithful Negroes" that white people had erected. I had read about them in my research of Eufaula and was curious. We found a lovely Jewish section, but no blacks until we asked the caretaker, who I was sure thought us two mad dogs rummaging around a graveyard in the heat. There is a Negro cemetery, but the headstones are gone, and who knows if anybody is even buried under the plain slope of grass where the ex-slaves are supposed to be. There are Confederates in the graveyard too, well marked and well-tended. I think about me poking around that town in Alabama in broad daylight with a white boy (well actually he's brown enough with dark hair and eyes, enough to be Latino, which in part, he is) and have visions of me dancing with him on those Confederate graves in a red dress.

Back to 431, on our way out of town, it is here we see again the high cliffs on the lake for which the town was named, Eufaula being the Creek Indian word for high bluffs. In the early 1800s some white men, brothers, saw the Creek Indians cultivating the fertile river-bottom lands on each side of the Chattahoochee River and saw that it was good. Word got out and soon other white men brought their families to the area to live and work peaceably with the Eufaula clan of the Creek tribe, or so popular history suggests. Whites moved in, Indians were pushed out, battles were fought, and the Indians lost. In 1819 Alabama became the twenty-second state of the Union. In 1832 the Creeks signed a treaty of evacuation promising them lands west of the Mississippi. It, along with every other treaty the U.S. ever made with the Indians, was broken.

Lake Eufaula is not a big one, but it's a long one stretching down to Georgia, a reservoir fed by the Chatahoochee River. We speed north on through Pittsview, past Hatchechubbee and up to Seale where we make a sharp turn off the Highway onto 26. We are going toward Hurtsboro, a half-horse town, so I can take John to Peterson land. I had been to Hurtsboro twice before. This is the third trip, and the first time I'm not with my father. Each time it gets a little less like a town and more and more like a color slide from a long ago vacation. Still at population 590 or so, it's one of only two incorporated towns in my father's home county.

Hurtsboro bustled when my dad was a young man in the 1920s and 1930s. Dad told me of how there used to be a feed store that did brisk business and a cane mill. He spoke of milling cane. Of watching the long green stalks being crushed underneath the grinding stone, or press, by 3-mule power. Of drinking fresh cane juice, a privilege bestowed on only those lucky few who lived near a mill. Of catching the smell of the juice as it boiled in a vat to make syrup. He would digress to the near-impossibility of finding pure cane syrup—nowadays it's all mixed with sorghum or molasses, which was wrong. Now what's left of Hurtsboro is a café, a deer-skinning business, and a hardware store, least that's all we see.

We drive toward Battle across the old Seaboard railroad line that once a day took travelers from Birmingham to Savannah and back again, stopping at every tiny hamlet along the way. We drive across

Battle Creek by way of Battle Bridge, which used to lay so low it flooded with a good rain and anyone caught on the wrong side of the bridge had to find shelter with kin until the creek fell. On the left is the old Battle cemetery, marked with a handmade sign, the place where my grandmother Annie Johnson is buried.

My cousin Tom Peterson won't go to that cemetery. John, Tom, and I are sitting in the home of Bennie Mae and Frank Johnson, residents of the Battle community for years, and friends of my father. I am related to Frank through my grandmother. "Won't go up there," Tom says.

"Why not?" I ask.

"I just don't go to that cemetery. Besides, there's snakes."

"But there's some good hickory nuts up there," Bennie Mae pipes up.

"I don't eat hickory nuts from there."

"Why not?"

"Look what they grew out of, look where the trees took nourishment."

"The graveyard!" we all say at once, and laugh, but Tom's not laughing. "There's snakes."

This obsession with snakes is not unwarranted, if I believe all the stories I hear. I haven't seen any—not a one. Under the guise of public service, people go about snake killing with a zeal that's just unnatural, weaving their snake-hunting stories into normal conversations. For instance, Bennie Mae and Frank are telling us about a church, a beautiful church, an old timey church somewhere not too far from Battle in a place off the grid called Zion or something like it. "They keep it nice." "They rake the yard." "They don't have an indoor toilet." "They use oil lamps instead of electricity." "Once a month they have an evening revival." "I've been to them." "They're real beautiful."

"Except I check underneath the pews before I sit down to make sure there are no snakes," says Bennie Mae.

"What?!"

"One evening a snake came in there so big it got stuck in the door!"

"What did you do?"

"We killed it."

There are all kinds of methods of killing. "I kilt it with an ax." "I clobbered it with a baseball bat." "I swung it around until it died." "I stomped on its head." This cold hatred of snakes, one that was not passed down to me, makes me feel weird inside. Snakes strike in self-defense, kill for food. Snakes don't ride through the night in posses in little white hoods and sheets, terrorizing the countryside. It's the rare animal that kills for the sake of killing. Humans are the only ones.

We see our own snake finally on our way out of Battle. John is stretching the legs of the little convertible down the two-lane road that runs through the land of my kin when he says "Snake!" My eyes, which were focused on the endless pines, ticked over to the road only fast enough to gain an impression of the snake. I turned around and saw the tail disappear down a grassy shoulder. John had not tried to swerve to miss it, the snake had not sped up to get out of the way. It was not an evil portent, we were not at a crossroads. Satan was not involved. Amazing what blind dumb hatred will make people do. I can't help but think of the Peterson boy.

It is night now and we are minutes away from eating enough fried fish to make us sick. We are hours away from the rest of our adventure. We are days away from understanding a New South, and months and years away from it not making a bit of difference one way or another. The sky is so full of stars it makes me giddy. I always wondered why you can see the stars better in the country. And when pointed out to me, I, being the city dweller that I am, always became defensive, making excuses for the defect in the New York City night sky. It finally hit me, while I was down in Alabama, that you can't see the stars in the city because the lights are just too damned bright.

It has to be dark enough.

Coda

For five days total we'll drive and I'll see stand after stand of Southern Pines. Old growth pine and new growth pine, and grassed over land filled with grazing cows that used to be fields of cotton, punctuated now by lone oak trees that look put there by accident. I'll see magnolia trees with blossoms as big as my head, a pecan grove that makes me think of church, wild plums and wild grapes-muscadine and scuppernong is what they call them.

We are speeding down 431 with the top down. John says he's not speeding because he doesn't want to get a ticket down there, but we are speeding, make no mistake. On either side of the two- lane highway are low embankments and trees. Above us and around us in panorama are thunderheads in size and shape not possible to view in our city. Ahead of us is the emptiest stretch of road on the Eastern Seaboard. You may find emptier out in Arizona or Montana. But this is it for here.

The top is down and we smell green and rain coming but we want to make it last, the wind pushing back our faces, the occasional bug caught in our open, laughing mouths, the cold damp, a coming storm, welcome.

We turn onto Route 26, at a sharp angle and quickly. That's the thing about the road signs down there; instead of placing the sign early enough for you to figure out that you have to turn soon, they place them right at the turn, so you miss it half the time.

Route 26 looks like an experiment in electricity, lightning stretching down to touch the yellow center line, leading us, showing us the way, to Battle and Peterson land, to my kin. "That tree is burning," John says and to our left, all alone, by itself, a pine is in flames, but it's a Southern Longleaf, not like the pitch pines of New Jersey, where I'm from. They need fire to pop their cones and release their seeds. For this reason they are called fire climax pines. I'm like those pines, waiting to release the seeds of distrust of the South. Succeeding some, but not completely.

derrame

Noel Quiñones

They call it the shoreline,
el abismo que tiene poder
too wide to hear plain truth
so replace your split frame
con un coquí cuya voz grita
Lo siento, la primera palabra
siempre es permiso. Its
bramble song, catching sand
in its test of boundary, forgive
its mythic forgery creada
a través del mar. What to feed
a schism of necessity que se
parece a un hombre, the halfbreed
coquí laments rain in el vientre de
la selva, drowns its limbs for not
knowing el ancho de su sed.
How sad, no puede hablar
Español? The room fills with
dirt / liquid, su abuela se ahoga
porque no podía salvarla.

Judging a Cover by His Books

Nelly Rosario

This annotated bibliography is a comprehensive overview of the titles most prominently displayed on the bookshelves—real or virtual—of the cosmopolitan educated heterosexual male of color whose intention is to seduce the bodies and minds of cosmopolitan educated heterosexual females of color. Jenna Lang of *The Guardian* effectively sums up his quandary: "How do you pick the perfect book to confer the desired air of intelligence and approachability, not to mention the combined sex appeal of Brad and Angelina?" Brangelina notwithstanding, Lang's question permeates all aspects of Said Male's lifestyle choices, from iPod playlist to faux-hawk coiffure.

Admittedly, the urbane heterosexual educated female of color should not judge a potential mate by the covers of his books. She can, however, endeavor to read between the lines and, thus, preempt future disappointments and shattered Ikea dishes.

The selection of titles is not based on the bookshelf of any individual. Rather, it draws from informal surveys of cosmopolitan heterosexual educated males and females of color alike about the predatory bibliophilic habits of the former. By no means is this compilation exhaustive, as it is also subject to the prejudices and proclivities of the bibliographer herself. Nor do I intend for this work to be taken seriously—least of all as blueprint for the aspiring Casanova or as syllabus for the lazy professor of literature or as ingenious marketing tool for any author and/or publisher. The reader is invited to adjust titles according to the ephemeral demands of popular and/or academic American culture. Furthermore, compilations of counter-bibliographies by irate males and/or cited authors are humbly encouraged.

For the sake of conciseness, the cosmopolitan educated heterosexual male of color will heretofore be referred as "Said Male." As this Euro- and hetero-sexist bibliography attempts to expose the psyche of a grossly proto- and stereo-typical character, I utilize APA format, per American Psychological Association standards. In the interest of narrative flow, items are not alphabetized, neither by author nor title. The resource material is divided into the following nine major subareas, though many of the titles can be easily cross-referenced:

I. I Have a Colossal Penis
II. And Yet…I am a Sensitive Man, Masculine Enough to be in Touch with my Anima and/or Child Self
III. こんにちは, Yo suis Mr. Internationale, Mio Amore
IV. I May Be the Second Coming of Christ
V. Count on My Visionary Virility When This Race Man Starts The Revolution
VI. I am a Horse in the Sack
VII. My Inner Geek=$m_{oney}c_{ash}^2$
VIII. I'm With It, Got My Finger on the Pulse
IX. I am Obama Beta

KEYWORDS: dating deal-breakers, dick-lit, hack intellectuals, oranges, biblio- and other -philes,pears, post-modernist tropes, Che-Guevara Complex, nutty professors, apples, STDs, academic spoofs

I. I Have a Colossal Penis

Tolstoy, L., Pevear, R., & Volokhonsky, L. (2008). *War and Peace.* London: Vintage.

Weighing in at over 1400 pages in most paperbacks, this tome is sure to elicit swooning in the cosmopolitan heterosexual educated female of color. However, the novel may signal subconscious Napoleonic complex of Said Male for its *broad* focus on the namesake's 1812 *invasion* of Russia. See III.

II. And Yet…I am a Sensitive Man, Masculine Enough to be in Touch with my Anima and/or Child Self

Rombauer, I., Becker, M., & Becker, E. (2006). *Joy of Cooking.* New York: Scribner.

That this classic cookbook (published over 75 years ago) is not displayed in the kitchen nor the least bit stained should raise a red flag.

Morrison, T., (2006). *Beloved.* New York: Alfred A. Knopf.

Everyman's Library edition, for every man who ventures to read highly lyric prose juxtaposed with barbaric scenes. Half-read by Said Male at a Miami beach during Freaknic, this freshman required novel chronicles the post-Civil-War life of a woman haunted by the memory of slavery.

Rowling, J., (2009). *Harry Potter* (paperback boxed set). New York: Arthur A. Levine Books.

The wizardry of the Harry Potter series, which Stephen King hails as "one for the ages," essentially translates here as: "I am in touch with my inner child—ergo, father material."

Rosario, N., (2002). *Song of the Water Saints.* New York: Pantheon Books.

Typical multi-generational, Latin-American family saga set during war and dictatorship, with a splash of coming-to-América. Book discussion often includes: "see, I read women;" "real steamy scenes;" "Dominican, like A-Rod and Manny Ramirez…" See III.

Cameron, J., (2002). *The Artist's Way.* Los Angeles: Tarcher.

A self-help book for the blocked and self-destructive artist. It suggests writing regular "morning pages" and "artist's dates," egocentric activities he finds unusually stimulating. Opportunity for male to discuss brilliant novel-in-progress, as well as to bemoan his sufferings as a struggling artist living in the hard, cold city. Good for trapping potential cosmopolitan heterosexual educated muses of color or otherwise. Due to the book's quasi-spiritual nature, also see IV.

III. こんにちは, Yo Suis Mr. Internationale, Mio Amore

Garcia, G., & Rabassa, G. (1998). *One Hundred Years of Solitude.* New York: Perennial Classics.

Oprah's Book Club Edition! Like Oprah, one is not alone in

owning the novel that made the world pigeonhole as a magical-realist every writer with a Spanish surname. Follows a century of a fictional village called Macondo, of men building castles in the air. The novel is as comic and tragic as the knock-offs it has since engendered.

Camus, A., (1990). *L'Etranger*. City: Gallimard Jeunesse.

The Stranger…in Français, mon chéri! According to Amazon, this 1946 existential novel "not merely one of the most widely read novels of the 20th century, but one of the books likely to outlive it." It follows a "disaffected, apparently amoral young man" who feels "[a]lienation, the fear of anonymity, spiritual doubt," with whom the cosmopolitan heterosexual educated male deeply identifies, you know?

Osborne, L., (2005). *The Accidental Connoisseur*. San Francisco: North Point Press.

Certainly not an accidental choice. A wine-drinker is not an alcoholic but a romantic man with worldly tastes in all fine things beginning with 'W.'

Dostoevsky, F., (2004). *The Brothers Karamazov*. New York: Barnes & Noble.

The true erudite must own at least one of the Russians. The intellectual, the sensual, the idealistic, the literary, the philosophical, the psychological, the religious, the familial, and of course, murder!, all come together in this preeminent masterpiece. As this is Dostoyevsky's longest novel, also see I.

IV. I May Be the Second Coming of Christ

Zondervan, Z., (2001). *GNT Holy Bible,* Good News Translation, Catholic Edition. Grand Rapids: Zondervan.

That this is the Good News Translation and not the King James version: make of it what you will. That this is cited under a single author with two Z's in the name: make of it what you will. That this is the Catholic Edition: make of it what you will...

Coelho, P., (2006). *The Alchemist.* San Francisco: HarperSanFrancisco.

Bestselling exotic and inspirational fable about a shepherd boy who through his travels comes to understand himself. Often thrust in the face of hapless visitors as a "You *have* to read this!"

Sultan, S., (2004). *The Koran for Dummies.* Indianapolis: Wiley Publications.

Implies deep inquiry into and respect for Islam, despite national propaganda to the contrary. See III.

Editors, T., (2009). *The Torah in English Text.* City: CreateSpace.

The cosmopolitan heterosexual educated male also happens to be part Jewish, he will have you know. Furthermore, he will clarify that the seeds of the Bible lie in the Torah and that Israel is the pebble in President Barack Obama's 9 ½-sized shoe. See III and IX.

Easwaran, E., (2007). *The Bhagavad Gita*. Petaluma: Nilgiri Press

Punctuates his monologue about paths of knowledge, devotion, action, and meditation with, "Hindu women are as beautiful as the scriptures."

V. Count on My Visionary Virility When This Race Man Starts The Revolution [Can also be cross referenced with IX]

Zi, S., & Giles, L. (2006). *The Art of War*. City: Filiquarian Publishing, LLC.

Merely owning this 25-centuries old book on Chinese military strategy and thought endows him with the superpowers needed for The Revolution.

Fanon, F., & Philcox, R. (2004). *The Wretched of the Earth*. New York: Grove Press.

Among the canonical works on international black-liberation struggle. Purchased for an undergraduate Post-Colonial History Course. Corresponding Cliff Notes not available, forcing Said Male to read book in entirety by research-paper deadline.

Mao, Z., & Mao, T. (1972). *Quotations from Chairman Mao Tse-Tung*. Peking: Foreign Languages Press.

Chairman Mao's *Little Red Book*, as it is known in the West, is sure to spark heady discussions of Marxism-Leninism, vinyl bindings, and the inevitable fall of Wall Street. An opportunity to brag about past illegal and illicit trip to Castro's Cuba. See III, of course.

Guthrie, W., (1989). *The Greek Philosophers from Thales to Aristotle*. New York: Routledge.

Said Male holds up a hand to drive home the point that, according to palm-readers, his long, knuckled fingers betray a philosophical mind.

Haley, A., (1973). *The Autobiography of Malcolm X*. New York: Ballantine Books, by arrangement with Grove Press, 1973.

Based on interviews conducted by Haley, this 1965 biography of the African-American militant religious leader and activist née Malcolm Little is a black classic. Says Said Male: "This changed my life, man, changed my life."

VI. I am a Horse in the Sack

Vatsyayana, M., Doniger, W., & Kakar, S. (2009). *Kamasutra*. City: Oxford University Press, USA.

Hindu religious treatise written c. 400, which Amazon hails as "more than a book about sex. It is about the art of living." Sadly, Said Male will trace the etymology of *Kamasutra* to *cama* (Spanish for bed) and *sultry*, as opposed to *god of love* and *thread/guide/manual*.

Miller, H., & Nin, A. (1980). *Tropic of Cancer*. New York: Grove Weidenfeld.

Miller divulges on life as an American expat in Paris. Explicit material. Banned. "Rawer than a mooing steak, a literary STD," exclaims Said Male. See III.

VII. My Inner Geek=$\mathbf{m}_{oney}\mathbf{c}_{ash}^{\mathbf{2}}$

Gasiorowicz, S., (2003). *Quantum Physics.* New York: Wiley.

Riddled with typos as it is, this text is priced at over $100. Said Male will drop formaldehyde-scented words like "degeneracy," "entropy," "quarks," "vector"…

Author, A., (2003). *The Chicago Manual of Style.* Chicago: University of Chicago Press.

The words "Chicago" and "style" inspire anyone to pick up this title. Said Male claims to use its typographical rules when writing lovemail.

Isaacson, W., (2008). *Einstein: His Life and Universe.* New York: Simon & Schuster.

There is a photo of Einstein playing the violin on Said Male's refrigerator door, accompanied by the following Post-It: "Genius. Rebel. Discriminated against. Did not speak until, like, 3 yrs old. Failed sixth grade math (?). Spiritual. Womanizer."

Cheng, R., (2007). *Practical Chess Exercises.* City: Wheatmark.

Said Male acquired first chess set after watching Laurence

Fishburne and Denzel Washington pensively fiddling with pieces in *The Matrix* and *American Gangster*, respectively. "RZA of the Wu-Tang Clan plays, too." See V.

Gates, B., (2000). *Business @ the Speed of thought*. New York: Warner Business Books.

The cosmopolitan educated heterosexual female of color will bite a knuckle and marvel: "Both money *and* brains?!"

VIII. I'm With It, Got My Digit on the Pulse

Bolaño, R., (2008). *La Literatura Nazi en América / Nazi Literature in the Americas*. Barcelona: Editorial Seix Barral.

Roberto Bolaño is the *New Yorker*'s latest toast to Latin-American, dead, male writers. "I'm probably the only one reading him in español—oh, you haven't heard of Bolaño?" See III.

Moore, A., & Gibbons, D. (2005). *Watchmen*. New York: DC Comics.

And not the movie, mind you. This graphic novel about a plot to kill and discredit costumed adventurers is one Said Male has actually read in its entirety.

Shakur, T., (1999). *The Rose That Grew From Concrete*. New York: Pocket Books.

Hardcover published by MTV. Collection of poetry written by rapper Tupac Shakur between 1989 and 1991. Prefaced by his mother, Afeni, with a foreword by poet Nikki Giovanni. Expresses the very angst Said Male feels as a cosmopolitan heterosexual educated male of color. See V.

Bukowski, C., (2007). *Women: A Novel.* New York: ECCO.

A Caucasian undergraduate who reads "only Bukowski, dude" put Said Male on to the author. Centered around the autumn life of a celebrated writer, the novel title conveys the kind of yin-ness sorely absent from Bukowski's earlier works. See II.

Diaz, J., (2008). *The Brief Wondrous Life of Oscar Wao.* City: Riverhead Books.

This Pulitzer Prize-winning novel by Dominican-American Junot Díaz oftens serves Said Male as a "two-fer," as its title can easily be mistaken for a biography of the Victorian-era writer, Oscar Wilde. The author, a self-described "ghetto nerd," raucously tells the tale of a 300-pound-plus "lovesick ghetto nerd". See III and VII.

Hemingway, E., (2007). *Four Novels.* Barnes & Noble.

Of course Hemingway. Economy of prose. Understatement. Stoic men who hold it together under pressure. Cool American classics, punctuated by the writer's struggles with alcohol and his idyllic times in Europe and Cuba. See III.

IX. I am Obama Beta

Carnegie, D., (1998). *How to Win Friends and Influence People.* New

York: Pocket Books.

This is among the tattered books that inconspicuously line the bottom shelves, in addition to *The Game: Penetrating the Secret Society of Pickup Artists* by Neil Strauss and random self-help literature.

Obama, B., (2008). *The Audacity of Hope: Thoughts on Reclaiming the American Dream*. London: Vintage.

While watching Obama soar to become POTUS, Said Male was secretly surprised to find his own excitement audaciously tinged by… envy. Other titles owned: *Dreams from My Father: A Story of Race and Inheritance* (Chinese edition) and *Change We Can Believe In: Barack Obama's Plan to Renew America's Promise.*

Franklin, B., (2005). *The Autobiography of Benjamin Franklin*. City: Digireads.com.

Benjamin Franklin, polymath of polymaths, "a mother of a Founding Father," according to Said Male: printer, publisher, inventor, politician, theorist, author, satirist, scientist, activist, soldier, diplomat, statesman. Ending on the year 1757, 33 years before Franklin's death, this autobiography is unfinished…

An Introduction to the Monster

Tiphanie Yanique

Thank you for that New Year's Day. That day the monster was on my back. But then again, the monster has always been coming for me. I'm a warm blooded person. Because of where my blood comes from. Island blood. Thank you for that blood and for that island. But I had never been so cold. The monster was in the air. Maybe the monster was trying to nyam me, eat me. But there I was. I was the kind of boy, and I was still a boy, who would come to wear sweaters in the summers of South Carolina. But I'd kissed my mother that morning and climbed aboard a plane. Nothing with me but a bag. One change of light clothes, suitable for the West Indies, a toothbrush and a razor… the last because my mother had heard that there would be no one there who knew how to cut my black boy hair. She hadn't thought about my needing a winter coat.

And thank you for that long plane ride where I was too excited to be scared and so watched the sky. And for that long sleepless bus ride where my fear finally kept me from rest. Thank you for this West Indian boy in a bus, me, not sleeping, but looking out of the window as it became winter before my eyes. Cold monster.

Did I clarify that it was New Year's Day? That the kiss was my mother's last gift? She was dying of cancer. Breast, though no one but me and a doctor from a different island knew. I wasn't allowed to tell a soul because cancer of the breast or the uterus or any of the part of the body we call private, intimate, sexual—the parts we use for love—cancer there was a shameful thing. And so I boarded that plane and climbed onto that bus, heading to my own death, knowing I'd likely never see my mother again. But still, thank you for the burn in my mother's breast. Thank you for her kiss goodbye that let me know it was indeed, goodbye.

I could tell you about my mother. I should. For even she is the monster—and her mother, too. I just want to explain how this goes. It's a journey, but you're not alone in it. You feel alone. But also you take the journey because you don't want the loneliness. People don't kill themselves over loneliness. Maybe they go off to war because they want to be left alone. Left alone and lonely. Different things those. But no matter to me. I didn't want either. Just don't be confused by my life. Or all these lives. I am so thankful for this journey. Thank you for my own memories and thank you for the memories that made me.

We can't outrun the monster. Run monster. Run. And girl, did they make us run that first night! The winter air like pins in my nostrils. I had a bloody nose before a mile, but kept running, because the drill sergeant was shouting and because everyone else was running, too. No matter that I was in short pants in air colder than my mother's refrigerator. Thank you, monster, for the short pants. Thank you for the ash on my knees that looked like a disease. Thank you for the blood in my nose that guzzled out and coated my mouth and neck and shirt and scared the sergeants just enough.

That night I shivered. So loudly that a bunk mate threw his blanket on me. Thank you sweet monster. Good monster. That extra blanket helped. I slept. But it started again and again. Every morning the blasted running. Every night the cold. And the sweating in the cold. And the sweat freezing me. And the letter in the mail before basic was even out, telling me that my mother was dead.

The question is what is at the middle. Of it all. What do you meet when you get there? I'll tell you, even though I shouldn't. Doesn't matter. You'll still have to do the thing to know it. So what's at the middle? Myth and magic, both. No shame in that. It takes a village to raise a child but an ancestry to make a marriage. I would never have made it to my middle if it wasn't for my mother dying and for my father being already dead. Because then I would have never have signed myself up for a war we would lose.

My father had been fighting a war his whole life. A white man, he was. From the continent. A proper American. But not white-white. Cajun, he always insisted. Had fought in a war or two. Seen nothing but combat. Finally too shocked in the mind and broken in body, and so found himself stationed in the Virgin Islands. But it wasn't sunny for him. Lived on our island but lived like he was already dead. Away without leave in no time. Made a half-breed baby, who looked nothing like him. Me. Then sat down on the bench outside of a rum shop praying aloud to die until he did. But even that I'm thankful for. Thank you, old monster, thank you for my suicidal poppy. I went to the American war to out-war him. But then my mother died and it was so cold and well...

That wasn't my true middle. No. We are the middle. This right here is the middle. Always. Oh and I'm thankful for that. Because though everyone was heading to die in Ho Chi Minh—I was not. Not me. It wasn't that I had connections. No Rockefeller father to save my backside. No joining the Air Force instead of the Army. We didn't even know about those ways out on the island. Army it was. Cold as hell at the base. No one could understand anything I said. I hadn't learned to talk yankee yet. So I didn't have to say a thing. All I had to do was fake sickness.

I'd been living with sickness for over a year. Close to it. My mother told me she never breast-fed me. Baby formula was just arriving on the island when I was born. Everyone thought it was better, best. And so she scraped to provide it for me. But then as a grown man I had to face her bad breast. The nipple sinking in. The huge red blister that took over. Until she dived into it, the blister and the breast. I was there taking care of sickness. Loving sickness. I knew it well. Thank you.

Black boy bile, they called it. In America, I was the black boy, despite my half-blood history. Coughing up spit. All fake, but it fooled them. It wasn't that I was a coward. It was just that I realized I didn't want to war with the history of my old man. I didn't want anymore to hold up my life to his and see if mine was stronger. Not after my mother died. I never knew the man. He didn't live long enough. He was my first monster. And I knew he would follow me. Has followed me. But with a dead mama... well. Well, I decided I wasn't going. I wasn't going to be the drink-until-I'm-dead father, this time of half-mongoloid children. But still. His story is mine because I lived against him. That made his life as much an influence as if I'd lived beside him. I didn't get that then. But now I just thank God.

America believed me. Even though they couldn't catch what I was saying. Even though I'd been a good talker back home. Talked to the down-island doctor. Talked to my aunt about what to do in case my mother did go before me. They believed I was sickly. Too sickly to shoot a gun. Too sickly to even look like a good target. So sickly. Me? My whole life I'd had a cold but never the flu. I'd sprained my thumb once but never a wrist or an ankle. Sick wasn't my thing. Until it was. Then faking it so well made it so real. Now that's how you know me. Your poorly papa. Your hypochondriac dad.

So for me there was no walking amongst green trees that might make me long for home. No blinding light just before the rat-a-tat of a screaming enemy. No warm sweat in my face and pits. My war stayed cold and quiet. I was put to ironing the uniforms of those who came back dead. I ironed alone and in air condition. Had to keep the clothes crisp. Ready them for their formal funerals. Easy work on the body. Hard on the mind. Because it was Vietnam times. And so you know about the many who came back dead. And so you know about the many shirts I had to iron. And so you know about the many monsters that lived with me. I never fought in that war. I ironed. And even still, thank you for Vietnam. Thank you for every collar. For every sizzle of the metal when it kissed the starch. Thank you for the dead that came home for me to dress them.

"Poorly Papa? I've never called you that. Dad, I know you miss Steven. Okay? But you're not dying over it."

"We're all dying, Sola."

"You really are a hypochondriac. But this is *my* divorce. And it's no one's fault. I mean maybe it's my fault and Steven's fault. But not yours. Or Vietnam's fault. Or whatever. Don't get sick over it."

That's my daughter. Not realizing that it *is* my fault. And my parents' fault. It's true, I liked her husband. I mourn that monster, I do. But I'm not angry. Sola just needs to know that this monster is coming for her. Is always coming for her. The undershirts hot from the drier. How I was thankful for the heat in that cold cold room. The whole story. No clearing of light and jungle of grenades, just a landscape of stiff shirts. Pants with creases that could cut you. Being sickly since then is the small price I pay. I'm thankful. I'm only sick now because I wasn't dead before.

So now it's cancer they tell me. Like my mother. What else would it be? Mine in the private prostate. The story of the monster on my back, the monster on your back, is not just one of fathers and sons but also mothers and sons and mothers and daughters and even grandparents and aunties and first loves and who knows what else. But it's all there. Meeting you in the middle.

When the government released me there was the Serviceman's Act, the G.I. bill they call it now. It was that or keep working heat in the cold. Pushing an iron was the only skilled I'd learned. Couldn't go back home to the island just then, there was no home there yet. I needed another thing to keep me company until I figured it out. I didn't want to be lonely and so I marched to Hampton University, where the black American kids went, like it was a duty. Yes, this is an American love story. Because on the first day of school the man said that thing that I gather now they always say: "The person sitting next to you might be your future husband or wife."

I was at the end of the row. I'd been unsure about coming to the big meeting and snuck in late. On one side there was no one next to me. I stared at the empty space for a while to think about that. No one. It was so lonely ironing all those years. No buddies to grieve over because they were dead. They were dead when they came to me.

But thank you for that New Year's Day. And for all the new years. I am thankful for all of it. Every bit. Because there in the great hall with that man talking about looking to our right and left… who was that man? I wish I could thank him. He spoke so well and so clear... I turned from the emptiness at my right. And there to my left was your mother. Looking at me like she'd been on a long journey just to get to that spot. And when she said "hello, nice to meet you, I'm…" I heard her accent. A Virgin Islander. Imagine that. First time I'd heard those islands sounds in so long. Sounded like my own mother.

Poor Girls' Palace

Leslie C. Youngblood

Our mother had been gone now for eleven days. Her longest recess yet. Recess is what I'd nicknamed her time away. That's what it felt like to me: She'd be in the middle of being a mother, caring for us, and she'd stop—take a break. Much of my time was spent trying not to trigger her leaving: keeping my younger sister, Renee, quiet, laying out her clothes for school, cleaning without being told. But it wasn't enough. When my mother would recess was out of my control, maybe hers too.

Shortly after Renee was born, I'd gotten used to my mother's absences. Some nights she'd return after a couple of days, apologetic and with a purse full of fruit-flavored candies. Her auburn hair, which had been wild and glorious the last time I saw her, would be stuffed under a scarf that hung along her back like deflated wings. Renee was usually sleeping. I'd stay up with my mother, an apple-flavored candy under my tongue, savoring the sourness that made my jaws tense, as well as my time alone with her. Those nights almost made her leaving bearable. I loved feeling like it was only two of us in the world. She'd let me paint her toenails while she polished her fingernails. I was careful of the nub on the side of her left foot where a sixth toe had been. I wish I had one, too, just to remind me that I was hers.

"Renee give you any trouble, Clarissa?" she'd asked, pronouncing my first name the way she did when she was happy, letting it trail off her tongue like a note to a song. And no matter how many hours it had taken for me to get my sister to eat or stop her from crying, I'd always say no. My mother never told me where she'd been, and I'd never ask for fear of her speaking the words that would take her away from us again.

When my mother went on recess, I'd learned to check her closet to gauge how many outfits she'd packed into her overnight bag. Most times she would take enough clothes for no more than a few days. But this time her closet was nearly empty—the hangers faced me like a row of bare shoulders. She'd tossed her overnight bag and had taken the one Samsonite suitcase she owned. Atop her dresser was an envelope. She'd stuffed several dollars inside and scribbled "for emergency" across the front, then smacked a scarlet, lipstick-stained kiss in the corner like a stamp. No way to reach her, no word when she was coming home. She'd slipped out while we were sleeping, so we couldn't ask any questions. That was just her way.

Whatever I had to do, I wasn't going to panic. I would keep everything in order and wait for her. It was summer, late June. Maybe she needed time to herself more than ever since we were home most of the day and she was out of work. I held on to the thought of her being on recess to keep from being scared. Everything that I remember about recess was a happy time. And like all the recesses I'd known, it would be over soon.

I was fifteen and had long since weaned myself from missing her. Or so I thought. But not Renee. She was only six and hadn't quite learned the duality of our mother. The side Renee was privy to was a flurry of wet kisses, whispered "I love yous," her breath a whiff of coconut rum. Even if the secretarial pool called her in, she'd phoned us a few times a day and tell us how eager she was to get home. In the evening, the three of us nestled on the couch. We were appendages of her, stirring when she stirred, drifting asleep next to the warmth of her skin, the three of us amidst the television's starlight.

Then there was the other half that I knew too well. That I tried to distance from Renee. The woman who sought her salvation in men. More than once, I'd looked on as she'd collapse into the arms of a man as if she was lame and he alone had the power to make her whole. In the morning I'd discover her naked on her bed, her body shrouded in a thin, cotton sheet, her hair cobwebbed across her face. I'd close her door and fix Renee and me big bowls of cereal. We'd eat in silence, trying not to wake her. When she came to, she'd go about her morning, barely acknowledging we were there. "Her girls," as she sometimes called us, were afterthoughts. If we tried to talk to her at all on those days, she'd just stare at us—especially me—and shudder as if she'd seen the end of her life in our eyes. Then, within the next day or so, she'd be gone.

I prayed that my mother's absence wasn't a sign we'd have to uproot again. She often spent our rent money when she was away. We'd moved six times in two years. Twice to apartments on the same street, one block down. My mother and I carried our clothing from one place to another. Aunt Ida, my mother's older sister, and Uncle Larry came to help. All the while, Aunt Ida didn't say much, just shook her head every time my mother was in her sight, like she'd do in church when she'd catch a glimpse of a woman with a wig too bright, slit too high, what she'd call a "wayward woman." The times that we've stayed with Aunt Ida, she'd told my mother she should leave us with her and go "get yourself together." My mother always smiled and kissed Aunt Ida on the cheek, thanked her for the concern, then kept us away from Aunt Ida for weeks, forbidding us to utter her name.

Before our last relocation my mother predicted to me, "You're going to love the new house." And she was right. I was besotted for a few days with the large yard, fresh paint, and windows that flooded in light. Then only to find the *new* house was full of the same broken things as the last: the pipes clanged and spit droplets of water; the secondhand refrigerator barely kept food cool and leaked puddles that welted the tile. And in the center of it all, the living room possessed a silver, asthmatic lung of a radiator that Renee eyeballed as if it were alive. But when my mother's mood was right, there was a happiness surrounding us that filled every crack in the walls. She'd crank up the stereo, putting on her favorite song, "Respect," and Renee and I were her backup singers as she out wailed Aretha Franklin. Or we'd all be The Marvelettes taking turns on a verse of "Mr. Postman." Renee offbeat, trying to imitate the cobra wind my mother and I had to our hips. During those moments, Renee and I were content. We wanted nothing more than to harmonize with our mother, have her melodic voice cocoon around us, live within our walls so we wouldn't miss her as much when she was away.

A few days into her eleven-day absence, I had tucked Renee in bed with lies about where our mother was, and when she'd return. The only bedtime story Renee requested was the one our mother read to her—Dr. Seuss's *Oh, the Places You'll Go*. I'd sit on the corner of Renee's bed, reading, but trying not to taint the lines with my mother's Lena Horne sexiness that was only appropriate for whispering naughty words in a man's ear, something my mother did all the time, and I, at fifteen, had done more than once. Sometimes the prickly feel of that beard against my lips would overtake me, and I'd stop whatever I was doing and wait for the sensation below my navel to pass.

As I read to Renee, every few seconds I glanced up at our window, hoping to spot the headlights of our mother's lime-green Buick. All I could think about was what I'd say when she came back to us. I tried to act as if her leaving us in spurts was normal when it was anything but.

For a while Renee was mouthing along with me. *It's opener there in the wide open air.* When she fell asleep, I stopped reading and envied her slim frame floating in my old pajamas, her dark hair and lion brown skin inherited from her father—who was different from mine—clashing against the white sheets, and wished I was her. That I could soundly sleep in a house of make-believe.

Then I wished something even worse—that she was never born.

Renee had cracked my mother. Or maybe I had done it. Maybe I was the one she never wanted and Renee just added to her weight.

Later that week, Aunt Ida called, and I told her my mother was at the grocery store. It was killing Aunt Ida to take my word for anything, and she would have popped over if she and my mother hadn't fallen out about her habit of dropping by unannounced. Soon, it wouldn't matter. Aunt Ida would stop over, patent leather purse in hand, feather church hat cocked slightly to the left, and sit on the couch and wait.

The last time Aunt Ida had done that, my mother stumbled in around two in the morning and cursed her out for treating her like a child and me for allowing her in.

"If you can't come home at a decent hour, I'm going to notify the state, and see what it'll do," Aunt Ida shouted.

"You wouldn't dare do that! You wouldn't dare!" my mother screamed, tugging at the belt of her white jumpsuit, her makeup running, and what I'd later learn was the smell of sex seeping from her.

"I'll do it just as sure as my name is Ida Mae Calhoun. Just as sure as there is a God who sits high and looks down low..." *She was serious then.*

"I do the best I can. I'm tired of you thinking you're better than me. You act like you don't remember what it was like. You remember, don't you? You remember!" my mother shouted, then she dropped to the floor. I stood still, waiting. Waiting for Aunt Ida to answer her. *What was what like?* But she turned and shooed me away, hovering over my mother, rubbing her back, and then cleaned her up like spilt milk.

When I'd all but given up my mother was coming home, her Buick hissed. I peeked out and there she was, auburn cloud of hair, body crouched in her seat like she was hiding from God. Thinking that she'd come inside soon, I wedged myself in the corner of the sofa. Our living room was sparse. One bulb out of three flickered in the ceiling light fixture, and there was a constant buzzing as if it were brimming with flies. The couch and the dining room table came straight from my Aunt Ida's basement. Unlike the first couple of times we moved, my mother hadn't bothered to hang pictures.

For years she had a painting of the Last Supper that followed us. Some evenings I saw her standing in front of it, head bowed, praying underneath the feet of Jesus. When we moved the last time, I waited for her to hang it, but she didn't. She'd left the Jesus picture behind, and something told me Renee and I were next.

But maybe I was wrong. She'd returned. More than ever, I wanted her to believe I was keeping up with my studies. Once she said, "I love you, Rissa, but if I had to do it over, I would have waited to have you. Or at least I'd have stayed in school. Big belly and all," she said and feigned a waddle. "Don't let no boy get in your head. No matter how much you love him. He'll leave you one way or another." I promised her I wouldn't, hoping she'd tell me more about her life, more about my daddy, but that was as deep as she ever wanted to go.

After close to thirty minutes, my mother hadn't come in. I was wishing she'd be proud of me. I'd kept Renee clean and fed, Aunt Ida at bay. All I needed from her was some reason why she'd stayed away so long. But the more I thought about what she was doing to us, the angrier I got. What if she decided this wasn't where she wanted to be again and took off?

I threw on a sweater and scurried to the car. It was a little after ten p.m. and people were still milling about. The shoebox homes surrounding us were aglow with porch lights. Greensboro had hit almost ninety-two degrees that day and heat was hiding in the breeze. My sweater was only to avoid hearing my mother say, "You flounce around with too much skin showing." Standing in front of her passenger door, I could tell the lock was up, but the door often jammed and had to be opened from the inside. I knocked on the window, then jiggled the handle several times before she leaned over, lifted it, and I slid in. Not knowing what to do with my hands, I plowed them under each thigh, then stared at the yellow rabbit's foot hanging from her rearview mirror, its tiny claws peeked through the fur. She switched radio stations two times, flipped the glove compartment open and rifled through it.

"You okay, Ma?" I asked.

Her lips didn't show the hint of color, which meant she hadn't worn lipstick at all that day. She didn't believe in letting it reside in the cracks of her lips or corner of her mouth. Her lips were either call-girl tempting or Holy Roller bare. She hadn't been in the company of a man in the last few hours. No scent. And if there was a whiff of anything, it was only Ivory soap. Perfume was the standby gift from her male friends, and she told me she couldn't remember which one gave her what, so she rarely wore any. Regardless, she'd tote the bottles with her every time we moved and align them on her dresser like tiny misshapen servants.

Not bothering to turn toward me, she said, "Things didn't go the way I planned."

"What way was that?"

"You wouldn't understand."

I resented being treated like a child after she'd left me for days alone with hers. But still I wanted to rub her back like Aunt Ida would do.

"I might understand."

She flicked a strand of hair that was creeping across her eyes.

"I had money for one thing, and I used it for another." As soon as she said that, the thought of uprooting again made me nauseous. With every move, we lost more of her. I couldn't stand one more story about how the new place would really feel like home. Couldn't tolerate her breezing through another rundown apartment, telling me to imagine how it would be. How the three of us would enjoy fixing it up. And we would. For the first week, maybe the second. She'd even plop a few plants in the dreariest corners of the house. Religiously, at first, she'd water them. Then she'd depend on me to do it. Hating that the plants were reminders we couldn't be stable like other families, I'd let them die.

"You don't have the rent, Ma?"

"I had it. I don't no more."

"Maybe Aunt—" She held up her hand so quickly the words I was about to say backed up. I swallowed hard, staring straight ahead at nothing.

My mother had been able to stave off eviction as long as she was letting our landlord, Mr. Thomas, do his personal business with her. A couple of nights a month, he'd stopped by to check on things. I'd take Renee into our room and hike up the TV's volume. What he needed to check on was in my mother's room. Even if I didn't see Mr. Thomas go in there, I knew it was him because as he came he shouted, "Oh, Jesus! Oh, Jesus!" I could distinguish most of my mother's male friends that way. Sometimes I listened for any sound from her. A moan or sigh that would tell me that she was enjoying herself—that when I had sex I was to enjoy myself—but either she didn't make noise, or the men drowned her out.

"Go wake up your sister. It's best we leave here tonight."

"Where are we going?" I asked.

"To my friend's house."

"Which one?"

"Don't you worry about that. Unless you got a few hundred stashed somewhere, just do what I asked you." At that she dropped her head to the steering wheel. She wasn't crying, but gasping as if she was too tired to breathe. I leaned in closer and put my hand between her shoulder blades and rubbed her. She quieted, and for a few seconds, I believed everything would be okay. I should have been better prepared for that night. The spell my mother had over our landlord didn't resonate with his wife who'd popped up at our door to collect the rent last month, dismissing my excuses the first time, and returning the next day, paying no attention to my mother's freshly shaven and oiled legs—what she called her showstoppers—her high heels, and her skirt that was way too tight and short to be worn for sitting around the house. My mother's hips were weapons.

The Thomases invaded our house. Mr. Thomas didn't speak, just slunk back like he'd never been a wet spot on our sheets. Though I'd seen Mrs. Thomas once or twice, I didn't acknowledge her.

"It's good to see you, *Mr. Thomas*. It's always a pleasure when you stop by," I said and stood next to my mother. His shoes became his focal point and his wife, now a little more irritated, declined, for her and her husband, my offer of a glass of water. She said "late rent" so quickly that it might as well been a name, "*Larent*."

When my mother tired of Mrs. Thomas's rant, she yelled, "Rissa! Go get me my purse." After rummaging through it she said, "Oh Jesus! What happened to that money I had in here?"

That "Oh Jesus" didn't shake him. While my mother was pretending she had money, I eased out of the room.

When I reappeared, I said, "Mr. Thomas, when you stopped by to repair the faucet the other *night*, I mean day, you must have left this." I dangled his Timex.

"Been looking for that. Thank goodness you found it," he said. All his wife's attention was on him. "I didn't want it to get scratched whilst

I was working," he said to her. "To show our appreciation, I'm sure we can see fit to give you more time," he said as he fastened it to his wrist.

But our time had run out.

My mother had raised her head, and my hand was still warm from touching her.

"What friend we going to stay with, Ma?"

Before she answered, a station wagon parked next to us. Even through the darkness I knew it was the chubby jaws of "Aw Fuck." If my mother had a steady man, he was it.

"How's school?" was the extent of his small talk whenever he was waiting for my mother. Sometimes he'd leave the latest Jackson Five record on the dining room table. But living with Aw Fuck wasn't what I was going to do, especially not with Renee.

What if he was just playing nice and he turned out worse than the one who'd never shut the door when he peed. It wasn't until my mother saw the bathroom as open as a barnyard while he was taking a leak that she started hurling anything she could at him. He didn't even bother to zip up, and Renee and I looked on as his dick flopped right by us. I was twelve, and it was my second time seeing the privates of a grown man up close. My first time was a few years before. The odd thing was that my mother was there then too.

"With him, Ma? That's where you're taking us?"

"You got someplace better?"

"Aunt Ida's. I'm calling her," I said and started out of the car. My mother grabbed my arm and clawed her nails into me. If not for the sweater, she would have broken skin.

"You listen here. If I thought that was best, I'd call her. I'm the one taking care of you and your sister. It ain't the other way around.

"How you taking care of anything? You haven't even been home in days." My voice cracked. All I wanted was to ask her where she'd been. Why she'd stay away so long. Hear her tell me she'd never leave again. I stopped talking and snatched my arm from her. My hand smacked the rabbit's foot. She reached to steady it as I dashed out of the car.

"Just get your sister up like I told you and start packing," she shouted.

As soon as I got into the living room, I ran straight for the phone. Aunt Ida's waswhere I wanted to go. Even though I'd have to deal with her convent house rules, Renee and I would be safe. Her husband, Uncle Larry, had been around now for five years. Tall and gangly, he was the night manager at Piggly Wiggly and always looked swallowed by his shirts, with his narrow head sticking out. Unevenly spaced teeth, an overbite, and crooked ears stopped him way short of handsome or even good looking. Once when we were staying with them, he opened the bathroom door and there I was in my bra and panties. "Sorry, Ris. Sorry. 'Scuse me," he said and blew back like he'd been sprayed with Mace, not linger like my mother's peeing friend.

I trusted Uncle Larry, and I could tolerate Aunt Ida. Most of all, Renee, wouldn't be living with a stranger. That's all that mattered.

Before my mother was at the door, I only had time to tell Aunt Ida to get over to our place. I slammed the phone down and sprinted to get Renee. If my mother was pissed off at the thought of me calling Aunt Ida, I didn't know what she'd do when she found out I'd done it anyway. Renee was up when I got to our room. Swaddled in her favorite shirt spotted with gold fish, she had already dressed herself, cuffing her jeans at the bottom. One of her ponytails was freckled with lint. The zigzag part in her hair was also her doing.

"Mama's taking us with her this time?" she asked.

"She wants to, but Aunt Ida is coming."

I told Renee to get what she wanted to keep, and she only grabbed her Raggedy Ann. She was used to leaving things behind.

My mother lit into our room. Renee bolted to her, but I continued packing. My mother picked up Renee and kissed her in pecks. I turned away. After telling Renee that everything would be okay, my mother told us she'd have a place in a few weeks.

"You had to go away for work, Mama," Renee said. I'd even forgotten I'd told her that.

"That's exactly right, baby," my mother said.

"Rissa was like the mama when you were gone."

"Well, Mama's back now. And the three of us gonna be as happy as ever."

"You mean four," I said.

She tussled my hair and gently massaged my scalp the way she'd do when her lap was my whole world.

"Just for a while, Rissa. I promise. Then it'll be the three of us again." That spell she had on men? She must have had it on me too. She brushed my hair with the palm of her hand then pulled me closer. Not much taller than me, the side of my face rubbed against hers. We shared the same coarse hair that grew twice as thick and long as most. My breasts, my hips, touching with hers, nearly as developed. The soft blue-blackness of our skin glowed under the bedroom light. Someone was supposed to love me, take care of me. I had to believe it was her. The three of us stood there and the only audible breathing was my mother's, as if she were breathing for us, living for us.

"It'll be just you, me and Renee again soon. I promise." I didn't say anything at first. "You believe me?" she asked.

"Yes," I mumbled.

"We'll give it about a month, no more than two," she said. That was all I needed. I tightened my arms around her shoulder, burying myself into the suppleness of her.

Then the police-like banging at the door interrupted us, broke us apart.

"Who can that be this time of night? I know my friend wouldn't knock like he's lost his mind," my mother said, eyeing me as she spoke.

I'd forgotten I'd called Aunt Ida.

"That better not be who I think it is, Rissa," my mother said.

The courage I'd had in the car was gone, so was the moment we were sharing. The fact that I didn't say anything, told her everything. She grabbed Renee's hand and they hurried to the front door, leaving me standing there alone...barely able to breathe.

I was losing her—again.

Contributors

Born and raised in Southern California, **Brit Bennett** graduated from Stanford University and later earned her MFA in fiction at the University of Michigan, where she won a Hopwood Award in Graduate Short Fiction as well as the 2014 Hurston/Wright Award for College Writers. Her work has been featured in *The New Yorker*, *The New York Times Magazine*, The *Paris Review*, and *Jezebel*. Her debut novel, *The Mothers*, was released in 2016.

Ariana Brown is an Afromexicana poet from San Antonio, Texas, with a B.A. in African Diaspora Studies and Mexican American Studies from UT Austin. She is the recipient of an Academy of American Poets Prize and a 2014 collegiate national poetry slam champion. An alum of Brave New Voices, Ariana's work has been featured in PBS, *Huffington Post*, *Blavity*, *For Harriet*, and *Remezcla*. When she is not onstage, she is probably eating an avocado, listening to the Kumbia Kings, or validating black girl rage in all its miraculous forms. Her work is published or forthcoming in *Nepantla*, *Huizache*, *Rattle*, *Borderlands: Texas Poetry Review* and *¡Manteca!: An Anthology of Afro-Latin@ Poets from Arte Público Press*. She is currently earning an MFA in Poetry at the University of Pittsburgh. Find more of her work atwww.arianabrown.com and on social media @ arianathepoet.

Cortney Lamar Charleston is the author of *Telepathologies*, selected by D.A. Powell for the 2016 Saturnalia Books Poetry Prize. A recipient of fellowships from Cave Canem and The Conversation Literary Festival, his poems have appeared, or are forthcoming, in *POETRY*, *New England Review*, *Gulf Coast*, *TriQuarterly*, *The Iowa Review* and many other publications.

Geimy Colón was born in Santo Domingo, Dominican Republic and raised in Brooklyn, Geimy Colón is a voracious reader; she lives to read to write. A writer and a teacher, she earned a BA in Creative Nonfiction from Sarah Lawrence College and an MFA in Creative Writing from Hunter College, the latter after a decade of creating literacy and science-based education programs throughout NYC. She is currently writing her first novel and a collection of short stories about the games boys like to play.

Naima Coster is the author of *Halsey Street*, a novel about gentrification, family, and memory, set in Brooklyn, New York (Little A 2017). She is a graduate of the Columbia University MFA program and also holds degrees in English and Creative Writing from Yale University and Fordham University. Her stories and essays have appeared in *The New York Times*, *Arts & Letters*, *Kweli*, *The Rumpus*, *Guernica*, and *Cosmonauts Avenue,* among other places. Naima has taught writing in a range of settings, from prison to after-school programs, summer camps, and universities. She tweets about literature, culture, and justice as @zafatista.

Ansel Elkins is the author of *Blue Yodel*, winner of the 2014 Yale Series of Younger Poets Prize. Her poems have appeared in *The American Scholar*, *The Believer*, *Oxford American*, *Parnassus*, *Virginia Quarterly Review*, and elsewhere. She has received fellowships from the National Endowment for the Arts, the North Carolina Arts Council, the American Antiquarian Society, and Bread Loaf Writers' Conference, as well as a Discovery/

Boston Review Prize. She is currently visiting assistant professor of creative writing at the University of North Carolina at Greensboro.

Anita Felicelli is a Tamil-American fiction writer, poet, and critic. Her fiction has appeared in *Kweli*, *Joyland*, *The Normal School*, *The Stockholm Review*, *Strangelet*, and elsewhere. Her essays and reviews have appeared in the *New York Times*, *Salon*, *SF Chronicle*, *Los Angeles Review of Books*, and *The Rumpus*. Anita is the author of the poetry collection *Letters to an Albatross* (BlazeVOX). She received a 2005 Puffin Foundation grant for her poetry, which has been anthologized in *All We Can Hold* and *Thirty Days*. Her stories have thrice been a finalist for the *Glimmer Train* awards and her articles have received two Greater Bay Area Journalism awards. Born in South India, she was raised in Northern California, where she lives with her family. She is working on a novel and short story collection. Read more at www.anitafelicelli.com or by following @anitafelicelli.

After many years in Northern California, **Marko Fong** now lives in North Carolina. He has previously published in *Solstice Quarterly*, *Memoir And*, *Eclectica*, and the *Puritan*. He plays basketball twice a week with other people who too old to be doing it and follows UNC Volleyball very closely.

Rachel Eliza Griffiths is a poet and photographer. She received an MFA in Creative Writing from Sarah Lawrence College. A Cave Canem and Kimbilio Fellow, she is the recipient of fellowships including Yaddo, Provincetown Fine Arts Work Center, Cave Canem Foundation, Vermont Studio Center, The Millay Colony, and others. In 2011, Griffiths appeared in the first ever poetry issue in Oprah's *O Magazine*.

Griffiths is the author of *Miracle Arrhythmia*, *The Requited Distance*, and *Mule & Pear*. Her most recent full-length poetry collection, *Lighting the Shadow* (Four Ways Books), was a finalist for the 2015 Balcones Poetry Prize and the 2016 Phillis Wheatley Book Award in Poetry.

Currently, Griffiths teaches creative writing at Sarah Lawrence College and IAIA (Institute of American Indian Arts). She lives in Brooklyn, New York.

Raven Jackson is a native of Tennessee and a Cave Canem fellow. Her work has appeared or is forthcoming in *CALYX*, *Phantom Limb*, *PANK*, and elsewhere. She attends New York University's Graduate Film Program.

Hope Johnson is a native of Lexington, KY. She received her MFA in Creative Writing at Lesley University and BA in English from the University of Kentucky. Among many, Johnson's poetry has been published in *Loose Change Magazine* and *Pluck Journal of Affrilachian Art & Culture*. Her academic work on Creative and Culturally Responsive Instruction can be found in *Charter Schools: Voices from the Field*. Johnson now lives in New York City, where she continues her research and work-life striving to integrate creative writing and fine arts programs into underserved schools with the NYC Department of Education.

Cynthia Manick is the author of *Blue Hallelujahs* (Black Lawrence Press, 2016). A Pushcart Prize nominated poet with a MFA in Creative Writing from the New School; she has received fellowships from Cave Canem, the Callaloo Creative Writing Workshop, Hedgebrook, Poets House, and the Vermont Studio Center. She serves as East Coast Editor of Jamii Publishing and is Founder of the reading series Soul Sister Revue. Her work has appeared in the Academy of American Poets' Poem-A-Day Series, *African American Review*, *Bone Bouquet*, *Callaloo*, *Kweli Journal*, *Muzzle Magazine*, *Sou'wester*, *Pedestal Magazine*, *Tidal Basin*, *Wall Street Journal*, and elsewhere. She currently resides in Brooklyn, New York.

Cecca Austin Ochoa is a queer fiction writer of Salvadoran descent. Her fiction has appeared in *Art XX*, *MAKE: Literary Magazine*, *Nat. Brut*,

Anthologized in *Pariahs* (SFA Press) and forthcoming in *IMANIMAN* (Aunt Lute Press). Cecca serves as Managing Editor for *Apogee Journal.* She is a 2014 Alumnus of Voices of Our Nation's Artists. In 2011, she received the Astraea Foundation's Lesbian Writers Award. She is currently at work on her first novel *Desaparecida* about a young woman adopted during the Civil War in El Salvador and raised in the United States.

Cynthia Dewi Oka is a poet and author of *Nomad of Salt and Hard Water* (Thread Makes Blanket, 2016). A 2015 and 2017 Pushcart Prize Nominee, her poems have appeared online and in print, including in *Guernica, Black Renaissance Noire, Painted Bride Quarterly, Dusie, The Wide Shore, The Collapsar, Apogee, Kweli, As/Us Journal, Obsidian,* and *Terrain.org.* She is also a contributor the anthologies *Read Women* (Locked Horn Press, 2014), *Dismantle* (Thread Makes Blanket, 2014), and *Revolutionary Mothering: Love on the Frontlines* (PM Press, 2016). Cynthia has been awarded the Fifth Wednesday Journal Editor's Prize in Poetry, scholarships from the Voices of Our Nations (VONA) Writing Workshop and Vermont Studio Center, and the Art and Change Grant from Leeway Foundation. An immigrant from Bali, Indonesia, she is now based in South Jersey/Philly. Her second poetry collection, *Salvage,* will be available in fall is forthcoming in 2017 from Northwestern University Press.

Princess Joy L. Perry is a senior lecturer of composition, American literature, and creative writing at Old Dominion University in Norfolk, Virginia. A 2010 Pushcart Prize nominee, her fiction has appeared in *Kweli Journal, Harrington Gay Men's Literary Quarterly,* and twice in African American Review. In 2011 she was a Tobias Wolff Award in Fiction finalist and garnered an honorable mention from the *Common Review*'s first annual Short Story Prize in the summer of 2010. She is a past recipient of a Virginia Commission for the Arts Fellowship and a winner of the Zora Neale Hurston/Richard Wright Award.

Audrey Peterson is a writer and editor, and the former editor of *American Legacy*, the magazine of African-American history and culture. She is completing a family memoir about her German and African-American roots that includes the search for the truth about her grandfather, a German officer in World War II, and the lynching of a young man in Alabama, who may or may not have been her relative. Audrey lives in New York City and works in the communications department at Brooklyn College.

Noel Quiñones is a writer, performer, and educator raised in the Bronx. A CantoMundo, Brooklyn Poets, and Emerging Poets Fellow at Poets House, he was most recently a member of the 2016 Bowery Poetry Slam team. He has performed at historic locations such as Lincoln Center, the Nuyorican Poets Cafe, and Apples and Snakes - London. His work has appeared in *The Acentos Review*, *Pilgrimage Press*, *Kweli Journal*, and *Asymptote*. Follow him @NQNino322

Nelly Rosario is author of *Song of the Water Saints: A Novel* (Pantheon, 2002), winner of a PEN/Open Book Award. Her work appears in various anthologies and journals, including *Callaloo*, *Meridians*, *Review*, *Chess Life*, and *el diario/La Prensa*. Rosario holds an MFA from Columbia University and was formerly on faculty in the MFA Program at Texas State University. At present, she does writing and research for the Blacks at MIT History Project and collaborates on *desveladas*, a writing collective engaged in visual conversations across the Americas. Rosario lives in Brooklyn, NY.

Tiphanie Yanique is the author of the poetry collection, *Wife*, which won the 2016 Bocas Prize in Caribbean poetry and the United Kingdom's 2016 Forward/Felix Dennis Prize for a First Collection. Tiphanie is also the author of the novel, *Land of Love and Drowning*, which won the

2014 Flaherty-Dunnan First Novel Award from the Center for Fiction, the Phillis Wheatley Award for Pan-African Literature, and the American Academy of Arts and Letters Rosenthal Family Foundation Award. It was also listed by NPR as one of the Best Book of 2014 and became a finalist for the Orion Award in Environmental Literature and the Hurston-Wright Legacy Award. Tiphanie's collection of stories, *How to Escape from a Leper Colony*, won her a listing as one of the National Book Foundation's 5 Under 35. Her writing has also won the Bocas Award for Caribbean Fiction, the Boston Review Prize in Fiction, a Rona Jaffe Foundation Writers Award, a Pushcart Prize, a Fulbright Scholarship and an Academy of American Poet's Prize. She has been listed by the *Boston Globe* as one of the sixteen cultural figures to watch out for.

Tiphanie is from the Virgin Islands and is an associate professor at Wesleyan University. She lives in New Rochelle, New York with her husband, teacher and photographer Moses Djeli, and their three children.

Leslie C. Youngblood received an MFA from the University of North Carolina at Greensboro. A former assistant professor of creative writing at Lincoln University in Jefferson City, she has lectured at Mississippi State University, UNC-Greensboro, and the University of Ghana at Legon, as well as served as columnist and assistant editor for *Atlanta Tribune: The Magazine*.

She's been awarded a host of writing honors including a 2014 Yaddo's Elizabeth Ames Residency, the Lorian Hemingway Short Story Prize, a Hurston Wright Fellowship, 2010 Go On Girl! Book Club Aspiring Writer Award, and the Room of Her Own Foundation's 2009 Orlando Short Story Prize. She received funding to attend the Norman Mailer Writers' Colony in 2011. Her short story, "Poor Girls' Palace," was published in the winter 2009 edition of the *Indiana Review*. The first novel excerpt was published *Kweli Journal*, 2014.

Born in Bogalusa, Louisiana, and raised in Rochester, New York, she's fortunate to have a family of natural storytellers and a circle of supportive and family and friends.

Publication of her first novel, *Love Like Sky*, is forthcoming.

CPSIA information can be obtained
at www.ICGtesting.com
Printed in the USA
LVHW090532100820
662758LV00007B/1016

9 781942 547051